What Happened to Our Wood

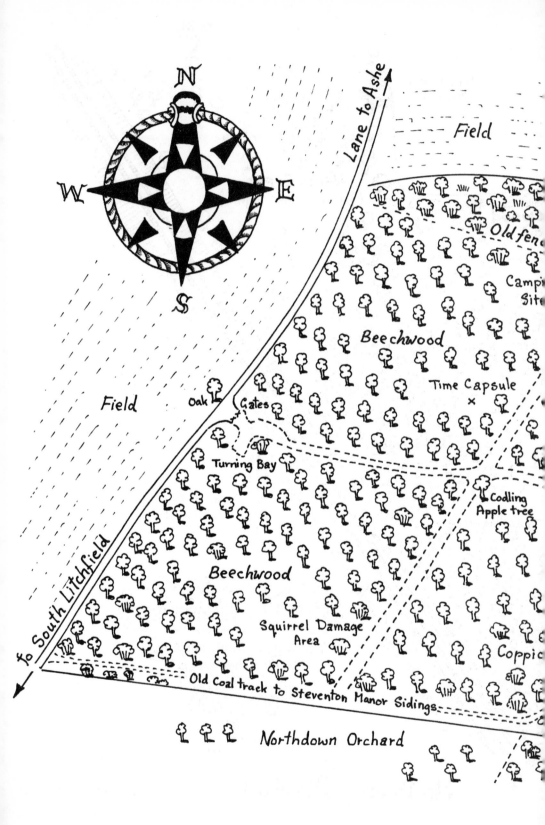

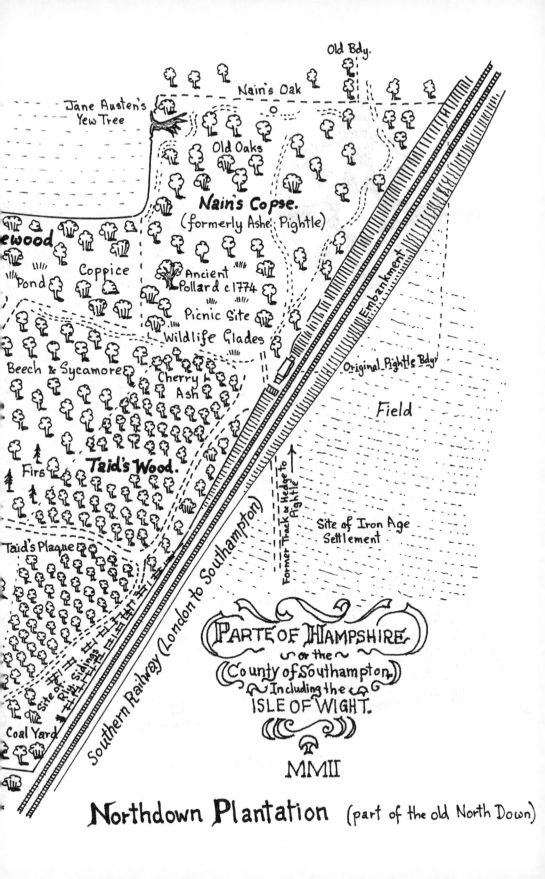

Jane Austen's
Yew Tree

Old Bdy.

Nain's Oak

Old Oaks

Nain's Copse.
(formerly Ashe Pightle)

ewood

Coppice

Pond

Ancient
Pollard c1774

Picnic Site

Wildlife Glades

Beech & Sycamore

Cherry &
Ash

Embankment

Original Pightle Bdy

Field

Firs

Taid's Wood.

Former Track & Hedge to Pightle

Site of Iron Age
Settlement

Taid's Plaque

Site of
Rly Sidings

Southern Railway (London to Southampton)

PARTE OF HAMPSHIRE
~ or the ~
County of Southampton
Including the
ISLE OF WIGHT.

MMII

Coal Yard

Northdown Plantation (part of the old North Down)

What Happened to Our Wood

The story of a small Hampshire woodland at the
end of the 20th Century

JULIAN EVANS

With illustrations by JOHN WHITE *and* STEPHEN EVANS

FOREWORD BY ALAN TITCHMARSH

PATULA BOOKS

2002

*Published by: Patula Books, P.O. Box 155, Alton,
Hampshire GU34 4WE, United Kingdom*

Copyright © Julian Evans 2002

ISBN 0-9541947-0-5

*Printed and bound in Great Britain by:
Butler & Tanner Ltd, Frome and London*

*To the memory of Margaret
and 32 full and happy years of marriage*

Bluebells

Foreword

This is Julian's second book about his wood, and it's astonishing that so much can happen to 30 acres in just 7 years. In a sense this is true of my own patch, also in Hampshire, which I planted in an open field in 1992. Today it is not a field with trees but a young woodland, with all the habitat that that implies, and with all the wildlife that comes with it. At times this growth is deceptively slow, but before you know where you are, a sapling is suddenly a young tree, and instead of peering down at it, you are craning you neck upwards.

Today, woodlands are as important as ever in our countryside. Great scourges in farming like BSE and Foot and Mouth Disease have pushed them off the front page, if ever they were there, but this makes them no less significant for our countryside. Indeed, one of the trends of recent years has been the upsurge in new plantings of native trees like ash and oak in the lowlands of England that will bless our children and theirs as well. Trees and woodlands are a backdrop, a canvas, a natural feature in which farms and fields, and heaths and moors, are framed and immeasurably enriched.

Another change of our times is the persistent shift away from forests and woodlands simply as providers of timber to multi-faceted communities of life offering homes for wildlife, for recreation of all sorts, and for enjoyment. The economic motivation is still there: indeed, history teaches that a working woodland is one that survives, and as a major timber importer we mustn't forget this. But fine, native broadleaved woodlands are good at satisfying just about everyone's different needs.

Woodland is not all that it appears. And this is the fun of Julian's new book with its enigmatic title. Good forestry practice sits alongside accounts of happenings and events recent—and for one delightful chapter—not so recent in the life of his wood. Seeing this diversity and meeting the unexpected, and then recording it here for us, provides the story and the intrigue.

Alan Titchmarsh, March 2002

Preface

My first book, *A Wood of Our Own*, is a hard act to follow. It attracted more interest than expected. The idea of owning one's own woodland struck a chord. Like that first dip in the sea on a summer holiday when once invigorated you get used to it, it's not long before the idea of one's own wood doesn't seem so strange. Indeed, the Press interest suggests that it is becoming quite popular alongside the resurrection of dry stone walling, elaborate tapestry work, and other occupations of an earlier time. But what has been unexpected, almost uncanny, is the variety of events and incidents our wood has attracted since writing the first book. I thought that just about everything that could have been said, had been. I was wrong.

Everything described in *What Happened to Our Wood* really happened. Only rarely have I had to draw inferences from the available facts and I hope it is clear when I do so. The gentle chronology that unfolded in *A Wood of Our Own* has not been continued, though all the main events since 1995 find a place. The continuing story is more a series of personal vignettes, sketches in the life of a woodland that ownership, management and writing about it have brought. It is a little like Rider-Haggard's *A Farmer's Year*—a commonplace book of all that happened in 1898. Here is a commonplace book of experiences of owning a woodland in the closing years of the last century and start of the present.

I must add a note about units. Both metric and imperial units are used in what seems most natural in the context. Such a mix is typical of us in Britain!

Why write another book? The incidents themselves seem reason enough, several people have asked to know what happened next, and, personally, I have enjoyed sharing the fun as well as the vicissitudes of caring for a small wood. It remains an uncommon experience, but one about which I am enthusiastic, and one which is accessible perhaps to more people than might appear at first sight. I also asked Margaret my wife the same question. Her thoughts were much as I've noted, but then she exclaimed: 'What else would I do on holiday?'

Sadly, so sadly, Margaret is no longer with us. I have left the Preface above and, indeed, the book itself as it had been written. But now it is dedicated to her and a Postscript is added.

I must also add how very grateful I am to Vanessa Whitting, who originally copy edited *A Wood of Our Own* and now this text, for encouraging me to continue with *What Happened to Our Wood* after Margaret's death. She emailed to say: 'Having read the two books, it's obvious what a partner she has been to you, in every sense. Although I don't know either of you, it seems to me that proceeding with the book will be a good thing because she was so much a part of the wood.'

Julian Evans
2002

Acknowledgements

I am pleased to acknowledge the assistance of many people, but recognise that the names listed here are inevitably incomplete: Jenny Claridge, Gerry Dutton, Colin Gee, John Newcomb, John Parker, and Alan Purkiss.

Permission was kindly given to reproduce two poems: by Lindsay (in chapter 7) and by Anne Wolfe (in chapter 17) for *The Grey Squirrel* by Humbert Wolfe from *Kensington Gardens*, Ernest Benn, 1924. Permission was also kindly given by signalling historian, George Pryer, to reproduce the railway track and sidings diagrams in chapter 3.

I am most grateful to all of the following who were involved in a similar way with the previous book about the wood, *A Wood of Our Own*. John White and my son, Stephen, for the beautifully crafted sketches that so embellish the book. Alan Titchmarsh for generously providing an appropriate Foreword. My brother-in-law and his wife for giving me permission to reveal some more of the wood's finances. My mother, my sister, Marilyn, and my brother, Martin, were pleased for me to include two illustrations sketched by my father.

Finally, many others who are named in the narrative or have helped in various ways are gratefully acknowledged for enriching the experience of owning a wood. Most of all I thank my late wife for encouraging me with this second book and who is so much part of the story.

Contents

Contents

1

The bomb

The remark was as unexpected as the setting was unexceptional. I was totally unprepared. We were in a drab students' lounge at York University, both of us having escaped for a coffee from discussions about sustainable tree-growing at a forestry conference, and Andrew opened with this remark: 'Julian, your book has caused me so much trouble!' I frowned and looked quizzical, if that's possible drinking what masqueraded for coffee from one of those impossible plastic cups. Relief of thirst was replaced by disbelief at Andrew's story.

My wife, her brother, and I had bought a small woodland in 1985. It was 22 acres of mixed pine and beech plantations some 27 years old, to which was added in 1994 a further 7½ acres of coppice with standards and a patch of scrub. In our first ten years, which forms the story of *A Wood of Our Own*—presumably the offending book referred to by Andrew—we hadn't had a single brush with the law. But that was soon to change. As searches of the wood were made by dogs and police teams in the autumn of 1996, the wider consequences of ownership, hitherto undetected and unsuspected, were certainly exposed. That episode was neither our first nor our only contact with the police. What I now relate is second-hand, having learned of it directly from the unsuspecting recipient himself. It is also secondhand as the incident concerned the book about the wood, rather than about the wood itself, which is the theme of this story.

A Wood of Our Own was quite widely bought and read including by fellow foresters and colleagues. One such, the late Kenneth Rankin, was greatly taken by my description of him in chapter 1 as 'the father of modern private forestry' and he delighted in buying 55 copies to give to friends and acquaintances, smitten as he was with investing in woodlands. The author was delighted too, and one chilly January afternoon in 1996 I suitably autographed the title page of each of the 55 copies in the study of Kenneth's Odiham home before they were dispatched for posting. During that afternoon, as we chatted of years gone by, Kenneth's enthusiasm was as infectious as ever. He had set up dozens and dozens of woodland and forest-owning syndicates across Britain and even as far a field as Australia. I use the past tense since in April of that year Kenneth died. He had rejoiced in the epithet 'father of modern private forestry' and to see it in print, and that Thursday afternoon showed once again just how true it was. It was to many of these syndicate members and new owners of woodlands that Kenneth sent my book.

While I signed the copies, Kenneth wrote out the address labels and stuck them on to jiffy bags just big enough to hold the book snugly. Some were used jiffy bags with creases and scuffed at the edges, others were new ones, but all were carefully and correctly addressed in Ken's slightly shaky hand of 86 years vintage. Over the next few days he took the bags to the post, or more accurately his wife mostly did so since he wasn't very well at the time. The relevance of all this will soon become clear.

One of the used jiffy bags containing *A Wood of Our Own* was addressed to Andrew Jennings, formerly a director of Economic Forestry Group which was one of the companies Kenneth had founded back in the 1950s. The package arrived sometime in February and, like all the ones Kenneth sent, it wasn't expected as it was intended to be a surprise gift. Andrew certainly wasn't expecting a jiffy bag through the post weighing about a pound and was curious, indeed, faintly suspicious, being actively and publicly involved with field sports. Whether he had been briefed about suspect packages—as we were at the Forestry Commission's research station where I worked—I don't know, but this is what he told me that day during the coffee break at York University in April 1996. It was all because of the jiffy bag.

The jiffy bag had arrived by the morning post. Andrew was suspicious and decided to ring the police. He was interrogated over

The bomb

the phone: Yes, it was a scruffy, used jiffy bag; yes, the address was hand written with uncertain, spidery capitals; yes, it probably did weigh about one pound; no, the postmark wasn't legible; no, the sender had not put a return address on the back or anywhere else; and no, such a package was not expected by the Jennings' household. With each reply, unease mounted. The sum of suspicious circumstances precipitated urgent instructions to carry the suspect parcel, ever so gently and ever so carefully, round to the back of the house and leave it in the field, a safe distance away. The bomb squad would be on their way immediately – indeed, they would be there in a jiffy!

The end of the story is anti-climactic. The two bomb squad officers carefully and surgically cut open the dun-coloured, well-used jiffy bag with a long-arm calliper only to find inside my book duly signed, and a note of greeting from Andrew's very old friend, Kenneth Rankin. The suspect bomb was just a book whose story is as gentle a rural caper as can be imagined, with nothing more explosive than the gamekeeper's shotgun or the 20 fire extinguishers dumped by some lout at the entrance, and nothing more suspicious than the unresolved matter of who sawed through the padlock on the gate.

At least the parcel hadn't been blown up and Andrew was able to enjoy the story of the book. He now enjoys relating the episode with the bomb squad, but it wasn't amusing at the time. Indeed, these days we cannot be too careful as, regrettably, there are always some who seek to get their way through less than democratic means. This was why in August 1996 I received a call from the British Transport police, all because of the sawn padlock.

My wife, Margaret, gave the detective my office phone number. It was a bad line, but amidst basic budgets and scientific papers on forestry, questions were put about who owned our wood, what it was for and had there been any unusual events in the last few weeks. The reason behind the questions was not explained and later that day, summoned to a meeting, the interrogation resumed in our living room and ended with my giving and signing a witness statement. It is strange to be quizzed about something you are familiar with and to offer replies and comments without knowing what is behind the questioning. The closest parallel is an immigration officer's sometimes bizarre enquiries about one's reasons for wanting to enter their country: you wait apprehensively as your name, passport number and other details are entered into the computer and checked against some vast database of names (presumably of prohibited persons, known criminals and other undesirables). While no threat of denied entry appeared to lurk behind the detective's courteous enquiries, the same feelings of uncertainty and faint disquiet were present. Several times he returned to the matter of the sawn padlock. In all probability it had been cut by a lorry driver making a late pick up of logs, but there is no proof. And, to my surprise, no reference to this severing of the padlock occurs in the woodland notes to confirm the date when it was first found cut. The notes are a succinct record kept of each visit and here was a chance for them to come into their own in the cause of justice—beyond, of course, being the irreplaceable resource for setting down here the story of our wood and all that's happened, expected and most unexpected—and they let us down! So I couldn't confirm the exact date. Nevertheless, the detective appeared satisfied with the explanation about the padlock and that it had been cut quite a long time ago, and why it hadn't been replaced. In fact, the sawn-through shank allows the gate's chain and locks to be opened easily and both Railtrack and I rely on the convenience it offers to open the gates

Before he left, the detective produced a videofit picture. A mysterious, unknown face looked out. I was still given no clue to what the investigation and questioning was all about.

Permission was requested to search the wood. Of course one has no choice, but it was formally given nonetheless. Questions were asked about what features and objects the police search team might encounter. There were the metal hoppers used to dispense bait for controlling grey squirrel numbers, the odd bits of rusting, corrugated iron sheeting for covering pheasant feed left from the days when the wood was keepered, and assorted rubbish consisting of an old fridge, a tin of sump oil, and other detritus still disfiguring the entrance. A plan was requested showing our boundaries, internal subdivision of the wood, and who our neighbours were.

When next at the wood a couple of weeks later, signs of a painstaking search were obvious. Mike, our organic market gardening neighbour, confirmed that on two occasions teams of police with several dogs had combed through the trees and undergrowth. They had questioned him too. The obvious signs, at least to me, were that every bit of rubbish, old plastic bags, the corrugated iron sheets, and so on had been disturbed or turned over.

Soil was exposed, rotten logs faced upwards though the slugs, woodlice and beetles, unaccustomed to exposure, had already departed for the safety of the dark and damp, and piles of branches, sticks and other trimmings—brash—were disentangled and scattered as if some moody kid had kicked about carefully piled floor sweepings. And the banks of the new pond were riddled with tiny holes.

Ben, my youngest son, and I found all this on the first visit after the police interrogation. We had gone to work on the new pond to excavate further and tidy the surroundings. Like spotted dick, but without the essential custard, we found the rounded landscaped banks were pitted all over. Numerous worm-sized holes perforated the sides as if in readiness for some chaotic peg-board game. The banks, shaped like small ancient burial mounds, had been investigated not by archaeologists but by police. Every couple of feet probes must have penetrated each bank's interior, feeling for its secrets. They would have penetrated, even perforated, the pond's lining of heavy black polythene that is all too easily pierced. Clearly the police were curious about the freshly constructed pond and wondered whether the mounds hid more than the chalk and subsoil from the hours of toil a couple of months before. They would have found a soggy layer of old newspapers under the pond's lining, but nothing more precious or incriminating. Our musings about this as Ben and I set to work were abruptly cut short.

Walking up the path which divides Nain's Copse from Northdown Plantation were three people: a tall determined woman in a dark navy blue trouser suit which accentuated her slight limp, and two middle-aged men much less smartly turned out. Even before I could ask them what they wanted, we became the focus of the interrogation. What were we doing, why were we here, when were these mounds (the pond's banks) constructed? I explained who I was, introduced Ben, and learned firsthand how the police searches were going. The impressive, almost imperious, lady was the senior police officer overseeing the day's search of undergrowth and scrub and she explained that there were several officers in the wood along with some dogs. They expected to take much of the day. If they found nothing they would still want to return once or twice in the ensuing weeks. Little was volunteered about why the wood was being searched, or what exactly they were looking for, and it would be idle to speculate here. Mike, my neighbour, heard talk of a train driver spotting someone loitering near the entrance to Litchfield tunnel, which is a few hundred yards from the wood, and of a suspicious car in the area, but nothing more substantial. Eventually the detective who had first been in touch phoned to say that nothing of substance had been found.

Since the autumn of 1996 police interest has receded. Certainly the hallmark of disturbed rubbish has not been in evidence and I haven't been interrogated again, at least not in connection with the wood. The pond didn't fill up with water very much due to the dry winter and perhaps the probing of its banks. For several weeks our woodland idyll was disturbed. Affairs of the wider world intruded, privacy was invaded, and a wood of our own became the focus of others' interest. And this wasn't our only brush with the law.

One December morning in 1995 I was repairing the gate—yet another lorry had doubtless found the bell-mouth entrance a shade too tight for turning—when a police traffic control car pulled in. It neatly straddled the entrance blocking any escape. An officer got out and, towering over me, asked 'Are you Julian Evans?' Now soap opera dialogue invariably has it that, when addressed by name in this way by police, some far-reaching consequence is destined. Either an arrest immediately follows, or an issue of a search warrant, or a request to accompany the officer to the police station. I didn't know what to make of this enquiry about who I was. I slowly uncurled and straightened up, dishevelled and hammer in hand, having been bending down to repair the broken bottom-most bar of the gate. The officer's tone of voice was firm but not suggestive of imminent arrest (not that I've ever had the experience) but how did he come to know my name, and why?

The occupant of the patrol car turned out to be our new neighbour, Alan Purkiss, who had recently acquired the three-acre wood that abuts onto the northern edge of Nain's Copse. A few weeks before I had had cause to visit this wood. Hurrying homeward in the car along Waltham lane, I noticed a woman in this policeman's new wood gathering armfuls of snowdrops. She had found a glorious patch just under the hedge about 30 yards in from the entrance. I braked hard, rapidly came to a halt, reversed up the lane with gearbox whining, pulled off in the entrance to the field opposite and hurried over to investigate. These precipitate actions didn't go unnoticed, and perhaps were even threatening, since she quickly stopped what she was doing and hastily explained that she wasn't stealing, this was her own wood. Indeed, as we exchanged greetings and found we were neighbours, Barbara, Alan's wife, explained that the snowdrops, in the absolute peak of condition, were being used to decorate the church. Later on she was planning an Easter event in their wood for the Sunday school. So they were already sharing their wood, and the blessings of God's handiwork, in ways that we too had come so much to appreciate. We were bound to meet our neighbours sometime, but the manner of meeting was a surprise and remains fresh in the memory. I suppose I was a surprise too, screeching to a halt on Waltham Lane and hastening to challenge a rapacious gatherer of wild flowers. At least I hadn't been in a police patrol car.

The Purkiss's look after their wood more tidily than we do. If we hear each other at work we usually meet up to garner local news and other intelligence that may impact our properties. On one occasion Alan, who was interviewed by the same British Transport Police detective, told us that it was not the first time that searches had been made of our woodlands. In the 1960s a girl was murdered on a train travelling up, it is thought, from Micheldever to Basingstoke. It was brutal and gory. When, at Basingstoke station, the body was found in the carriage there was much blood and her back was covered in stab wounds. Every inch of the lineside along the entire 18¾ mile run back to Micheldever, including the stretch near the old Waltham signal box where the wood is, was searched on foot for the murder weapon, presumed to be a knife. Searches were even extended further down the line to Winchester, but nothing was found and the case remains unsolved.

A surprise for us has been that the law and its long arm has touched our lives simply because we own a wood and write a story about it. But that is the interest and variety woven into life's tapestry. No other copies of the book suffered the indignity of bomb squad investigation. And no other secrets lie undetected in our wood as far as we know.

However, one secret is revealed in this chapter that remained hidden throughout the story in *A Wood of Our Own*, and a secret that several readers asked about. What is the name of the wood, besides the parts we ourselves decided to call Taid's Wood and Nain's Copse? It is 'Northdown Plantation'. Why 'Northdown' is explained in chapter 3: why 'Plantation' is because the wood was first established by planting on open farmland sometime in the 1880s or 1890s. It continued as a true plantation when acquired by the Forestry Commission in the 1950s who replanted the wood, after wartime fellings left it devastated, to pine and beech for the second crop.

The wood's name was not the only query raised. Indeed, telling the story raised many more questions. Foresters, especially, wanted to know more about the wood's profitability. Can a small wood like ours be financially worthwhile? So, with the approval of my co-owners (my wife, my brother-in-law and his wife) chapter 9 displays as much of our balance sheet as records permit. Also a few things in *A Wood of Our Own* need correcting. Mostly, however, this story relates the events and happenings, expected and unexpected, which have touched our 30-acre woodland and the lives of its owners. The story is like a series of personal vignettes, sketches in the life of a woodland that ownership and management has brought. But first a short chapter about what happened in our first 10 years as stewards of the wood, bombs and bobbies notwithstanding.

Snowdrops

2

What had happened before

We bought Northdown Plantation in April 1985. John, my wife's brother, and I had shared the cost equally and became owners of 22 acres of mixed pine and beech woodland. In fact we had become owners of it only for the next 967 years since what we bought was the residue of the Forestry Commission's 999 years lease. They had acquired it from the Steventon estate in the early 1950s. In 1994 we added to Northdown Plantation when Margaret and I bought the adjoining 7½ acres abutting the northern boundary and, at the same time, we acquired the freehold over the whole area.

Acquiring the freehold wasn't strictly necessary for carrying out forestry operations—and we weren't complaining about only having 967 years at our disposal—but as lessees we had no control over shooting for game. Although conflict between us and the sporting tenants was limited to staying out of the wood on shooting days, the main concern was that gamekeepers would put down winter feed for pheasants. This feed also sustained the wood's worst pest—grey squirrels.

Usually wheat or corn would be dispensed liberally from large drums or from specially designed feeders. Several would be installed from mid-October to January to attract pheasants into the wood and keep them there well fed. Pheasants are made to feel at home until the day the beaters arrive to flush them from the cover where they become easy quarry for the assembled guns as, unfit and overweight, they struggle to fly. The trouble was that grey squirrels also stayed well fed during the long winter months, producing larger broods of young ready for the coming summer's assault on our trees.

In the early 1990s grey squirrels caused more damage in the wood than any other creature. The main crop of beech trees was their prime target. Beech, along with oak and sycamore, are especially attractive to squirrels, particularly when aged from about 10 to 40 years old: and those of Northdown Plantation were in their 30s. Grey squirrels do their damage by stripping bark. Their sharp incisors quickly tear off flakes or strips of bark, which they are particularly adept at doing when seated comfortably. Thus most stripping occurs on the main trunk at a branch fork, on root spurs or around the base of a tree. If this stripping encircles the stem, everything above is killed; it is no different from any other girdling and ring barking. Grey squirrels are quite capable of massive debarking in a matter of minutes. The bark is not ingested but spat out almost as soon as it is ripped from the tree. The animal is a menace to broadleaved woodlands in their adolescent years. Squirrel control occupies more time than any other single job needed in the wood, but there is no doubt that stopping the pheasant shooting, and all that went with it, has been a help. This furry, cuddly, cute—and wretched—inhabitant of the woodland canopy has an unexpected chapter to itself later; the squirrel wars continue.

We bought the wood from the Forestry Commission when the Thatcher Government's early privatisations were under way in the 1980s. The Commission began selling off small isolated woods, often far from the district office, that were inefficient for them to manage. Northdown Plantation was one such block that they had acquired in the early 1950s as derelict woodland, abandoned since being cut over to help the war effort. And what we inherited was the fruit of the Commission's effort to turn it into a worthwhile tree crop. They had largely succeeded and created a reasonable mixed stand of beech and Corsican pine trees from which they had harvested just one thinning of pine by removing every third row. They had built a fine entrance opening onto the lane that runs along the top of the wood. It included a wide mouth, gates, turning area and holding bay and a short track engineered to a standard to give access and support to timber-laden lorries. It was a real asset and one of the key features to look for when buying a wood—is the access good, will one be able to get logs to road easily or will they need dragging across a field or up a long slope? More than anything else, access determines value and usefulness. Poor access gives poor profitability.

The main crop of trees was 27 years old in 1985 when we bought the wood. This was a good age because all the hard work and long years of establishment were past and the crop was entering the productive stage of thinning and, in the case of pine, final felling in about a decade or two's time. Thus some income could be expected. This was always Kenneth Rankin's advice—he really is the father of modern private forestry having founded the Economic Forestry Group later to become Tilhill Economic Forestry. Ken, whose kindness led to all the furore described in chapter 1, always advised that one should only buy a wood someone else has laboured to establish; life is too short to see a crop through from scratch to final felling. And, by buying an existing woodland, some revenue can be expected almost straightaway from thinnings and perhaps even some fellings. Chapter 9 records our experience of this advice.

In the first ten years of owning Northdown Plantation there

were two thinnings of trees, one simply to remove the poorest ones for firewood and the second, several years later, to harvest all the pine. Felling the pine yielded a worthwhile parcel of over 600 tons. This almost recouped the cash price paid for the wood seven years before, and equally importantly gave room for the beech trees to develop. The beech trees are now the main crop but still have at least another 60 years of their rotation before final felling. In these early years of ownership, much of the wood was given a silvicultural cleaning. The best stems of beech trees were high pruned as were, belatedly, the better Douglas firs in the four small patches of them that amounted to no more than two acres.

At the bottom of the wood, beside the railway, was a four-acre strip that in 1985 still supported large trees that were not ours. This timber had been retained from before the Forestry Commission's ownership and did not legally have to be cut until 2003. Fortunately for us the then lessors, Prudential Insurance, decided not to wait and this crop was harvested in the winter of 1986 and the land vacated. John and I planted it in the spring of 1987 with ash, wild cherry and oak and named it after my father, Taid's Wood. Taid is Welsh for grandfather, my father being grandfather to our three sons and is pronounced like 'tide'.

At the northern end of Taid's Wood, indeed alongside the whole length of this part of Northdown Plantation's boundary, is an entirely different woodland. The opportunity to buy it arose in 1994, and to name it too: Nain's Copse after my mother, Nain being Welsh for grandmother and pronounced like 'nine'. Most of it is mature woodland, unlike Northdown Plantation's still youthful trees, a contrast of age encapsulated by the wit of our youngest son's friend, Ben Marnan, albeit not in a tree context. On the way to a performance of STOMP at the Chichester Theatre the question arose about the differences between the lecturers at sixth-form college and their old teachers at secondary school. Without pausing, he volunteered: 'They actually help you with your problems rather than shouting at you for having them!' Of course, this may reveal more about maturity of student than instructor.

A small part of Nain's Copse, forming a spear shape that tapers towards the lane, is largely a tangle of long neglected scrub with a few untidy clumps of scrappy hazel coppice. The larger part is square, or more properly oblong in shape, and is a coppice with standards, that is a coppice woodland with large trees, the standards, scattered through. About one hundred oak standards, aged between 115 and 160 years, densely overstood a coppice of sycamore and ash that was last cut in about 1960. When we bought this wood the coppice stems were drawn up, crowding the nearly complete canopy of oak crowns. There should have been a further coppicing and thinning of standards in the 1980s, but no work was ever seen or done in this wood. Thus in 1994 the first and urgent task was to thin the oaks, and 42 of them and one ash were cut. The tall leggy sycamore coppice was too far gone, too long 'stored' in forester's parlance, to re-coppice and a gentle thinning of their stems has been taking place ever since to create a lovely mixed wood of oak, ash and sycamore, converting it to high forest.

Two storms have struck the wood. The great storm of October 1987 brought down only eight trees as we were on the edge of the worst affected zone, but the wood was not so spared by the ferocious gales of late January 1990. These uprooted or snapped some 120 trees, including many of the biggest and best pines. It was one reason why the remainder were felled a couple of years later. Winter gales continue to snap branches, break apart forked limbs and overturn the odd weakened tree, but none has matched the destructive force of 1987 or 1990.

The wood's age and predominantly broadleaved composition renders the fire risk virtually negligible. Other damage comes from occasional resurgences of beech bark disease, the fraying activities of roe deer that frequent the wood, and, of course, the wretched depredations of grey squirrels. People dump rubbish at the entrance, pilfer firewood when it's easily visible, and throw beer cans and other ephemera from the trains that rush up and down the track that forms our eastern boundary. But on the whole trouble is minor. And now that trains are electric or diesel, sparks are no longer a fire risk either!

Much more could be said about the first ten years, but this rehearsal of events is brief since they are related in *A Wood of Our Own*, and because as chapter 1 has shown it is the last few years that have been so full of surprises. However, when we first bought the wood, Margaret and I did pray that it would be enjoyed and shared by many. Our prayers were answered, and it continues to be so, though not always in ways we expected. Also unexpected have been discoveries about what happened long before we owned the wood as more of its early history has come to light.

Writing the wood's story has, in a small way, extended the pleasure of ownership. As Sir Winston Churchill observed of his far,

far greater work of many volumes of second world war history: 'Writing a long and substantial book is like having a friend and companion at your side, to whom you can always turn for comfort and amusement, and whose society becomes more attractive as a new and widening field of interest is lighted in the mind'. Both the wood and the writing of its story are such friends, giving comfort and, certainly, amusement. The remarkable widening of interest and incidents has been no less true.

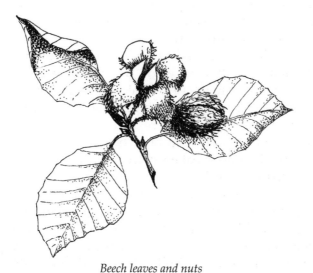

Beech leaves and nuts

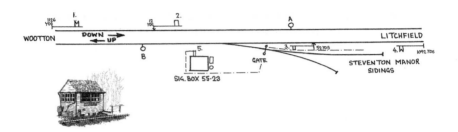

The key is at the signal box

The first edition ordnance survey maps for England, the Napoleonic maps prepared in the early decades of the 19th century, show no sign of our wood. Even Nain's Copse, which boasts oak trees at least 200 years old, is not marked, although nearby Bramdown Copse is. The early map clearly shows the crossroads where Waltham Lane intersects Burley Lane, the lane that after the crossroads becomes unnamed, and forms the wood's western boundary and goes on to the hamlet of South Litchfield. But on this early map, the land in the southeast quadrant of the crossroads where our wood should be is blank. I have even checked the originals held in the map room of the Royal Geographical Society. This fine room, redolent of past epics and episodes of discovery, is full of cartographical reference works, calf bound tomes, archived maps, sketches and plans, well thumbed and sometimes a little frayed or with pages foxed. The Society possesses the world's finest map collection not in public ownership, and for the wood's location, held several revisions of the Ordinance Survey first edition. Each revision incorporated improvements and amendments that were simply accumulated until the industrious Victorians finally brought out a second and vastly improved edition in the 1870s. A large grey cardboard map folder, the size of an artist's portfolio, containing originals of sheets 12 and 13 was entrusted to me and carried respectfully to a long display table. Gingerly, one by one, the frail sheets were teased out and examined. Particular attention was given to the 1840 version of sheet 13 that was the first to show the newly constructed London–Southampton railway line. This line is the wood's eastern boundary and with the lane running the length of the western edge, defines precisely its location. And there was clearly no sign of the wood, neither Northdown Plantation nor Nain's Copse.

Earlier research had shown that even the 1876 6" map of the 2nd edition OS map, Hampshire sheet XXV NE, did not feature Northdown plantation though the square shape of the much smaller Nain's Copse is clearly marked as woodland with two oaks specially highlighted. Northdown Plantation first appears on the 1911 OS map, a half century after the coming of the railway, and this had led me to speculate a link: eventually fields to the west of the new line proved less readily accessible to the rest of the Steventon Estate to which they belonged, and so were put down to trees sometime in the 1880s.

However, when the fields that became our wood were first planted they were not, in fact, part of the Steventon estate as had been supposed. Although this is the estate from which the Forestry Commission had acquired Northdown Plantation, in the 19th century the Steventon estate was confined to the parish of that name except for the tiny four-acre enclave which we have labelled Nain's Copse. Thanks to the researches of local historian Gerry Dutton, the tithe maps of the 1840s show that the field of Upper or Big North Down was part of the Litchfield Grange Estate in the parish of Ashe owned by one John Stephens and farmed by Jesse Vidler. Not until about 1910 did the Steventon Estate extend well beyond the parish boundaries. This was when it was acquired by the new owner of the adjoining Litchfield Estate, Robert Mills. North Down was Litchfield's biggest field (79 acres) though it was sliced in two by the railway to create Upper and Lower North Down. Gerry also suggested the reason for this name, and hence for Northdown Plantation, namely that this large field was simply at the northernmost end of the Litchfield Grange Estate. And 'down' is almost always pasture for sheep on hill or other elevated land.

This large field was once remembered for another reason. To celebrate the opening of the railway on 11th May 1841, a bullock was roasted at Micheldever Station, then known as Andover Road. And part of the roast was brought to Steventon, presumably up the new railway. It was eaten by the villagers in 'North Down Field' with, so the record goes, great enjoyment. The field was a mile and a half from the village, but the celebration was there because the line is level with the ground and not elevated on embankment, like the massive and impressive earthwork that takes the track through Steventon itself, nor in a cutting or tunnel as it is farther south.

The real reason for establishing Northdown Plantation may be very mundane. Agriculture was depressed in the 1870s and 1880s. Farmers complained of poor harvests and even poorer prices owing to cheap imports: nothing changes! The impact on Hampshire's landscape was a reduction in arable land, declining from 450,000 acres in 1875 to only 300,000 acres in 1913. Several other new plantations appeared in the vicinity of Litchfield Grange at this time, notably Warren, Signpost, Bellevue and Railway plantations. Perhaps these were all precipitated when Litchfield Grange Estate was bought in 1880 by Alexander Cunningham who in time sold it to Robert Mills of Shefford Park, Newbury with its notable Shefford Woodlands.

The tithe maps recorded something else: the well-timbered square of Nain's copse, with its unusual mix of oak standards and predominantly sycamore coppice, was clearly delineated on the maps, but not as woodland! It was at the western extremity of the Steventon Estate, owned by Edward Knight Esq. and tenanted by one Francis William Digby, and it was labelled Ashe Pightle. Pightle is middle English meaning a 'small enclosure', often of several acres, and usually located at the edge of an estate and is pronounced like 'title', though sometimes the corrupted form 'piddle' like 'fiddle' is what survives. It is commonly bounded by a thick hedge, sometimes with large trees spaced out just as Nain's copse has around its perimeter. When needs be, it would be made fully stockproof or subdivided with hazel hurdles. Gerry Dutton thinks our Ashe pightle was originally a warren for rabbits that later became a sheep fold. The railway, completed in May 1841, cut through the southeast corner of the pightle and irrevocably severed this quaint enclosure from its access track to Warren Farm, and the rest of Steventon. Inaccessible, and presumably lying idle, it was doubtless planted to create the woodland we have inherited and to explain why it appears as woodland as early as the 1876 OS map while Northdown Plantation didn't appear until two OS editions later in 1911.

When Northdown Plantation was acquired in 1985 the title deeds contained next to nothing about this or any of its history.

Indeed, the Forestry Commission didn't even know that an access right had been granted in perpetuity to British Rail and its successors in title along the main track through the wood! Inspection of the trees themselves showed what the Commission had achieved during their stewardship, but what had they had to contend with to establish the mixed crop of pine and beech we inherited? Alan Betts, the Commission's conservator of forests for southeast England, suggested where this could be discovered: the Commission's famous post-war census. It was good advice and led to a more modern and far larger room than the Geographical Society's map room, but one dedicated to the same purpose: Britain's Public Record Office in Kew housing what are grandly proclaimed as 'The National Archives'. Among countless riches is the entire set of Britain's most comprehensive survey of forests and woodlands. Carried out in 1947 it is one of those rare censuses that recorded everything and not just a sample. Indeed the Forestry Commission itself called it a modern Domesday book for woodland. Every forest and woodland bigger than five acres was visited and assessed. And every original field sheet is available for inspection at Kew, always provided you could plot the route to exactly the reference code for the archivists to retrieve!

It was my first visit to Kew Public Record Office (PRO). The easy route from Kew Gardens station is a 7 or 8 minutes walk to the main gates. From there, to the right an orderly rectangular pool greets you with a regiment of fountains playing, while to the left there is a more natural looking lake with its requisite island. Flanked by these water features, as the architect's plans would surely have called them, an occasional swan or goose challenges your right of way with all the stern severity a place of such gravitas demands. The building you enter is a many-floored grey-brown, concrete, block that rises like an inverted pyramid, and is really more appealing than this description suggests.

Inside you feel almost as lost as the archive you are hoping to retrieve. Happily the welcoming leaflet says as much 'The PRO is a big place, and on a first visit can seem confusing'. It can. Once your reader's ticket has been obtained the first step is to work out how the archive might be referenced, where it is referenced within the PRO, and then to identify with absolute accuracy the unique coding for the document in question. It took 30 minutes, first via catalogues, and then via microfiche of counties surveyed, to track down Sheet XXV of NE Hampshire Forestry Commission census record F 22/165. This was the unique code needed by the retrieval desk, a bleeper was issued in exchange, and then I waited to be summoned. I had arrived at 3.28 pm and reached this stage by 3.58 pm which was just two minutes before the daily 'guillotine' for retrieval enquiries of 4pm. I was allocated seat 8D, went to it only to find a young lady there closely examining a frail manuscript ragged at the edges. I dumped my anorak on seat 8E, waited, was soon bleeped and went to collect the precious census document. But I'd misread my bleeper, I was 18D. The archivists were expecting the young lady not a bearded professor, patently absent-minded. They smiled. Amused rather than embarrassed, the anorak was hastily retrieved from 8E. A little later, and properly ensconced, 18D was bleeped. At the desk, a beige coloured folder, some 2 inches thick, that was record F 22/165 was handed over. Quick examination led to the field sheets for stands 8, 9 and 10 which were the ones covering Northdown Plantation and Nain's Copse.

For this great census each forest or woodland stand was assessed and recorded on demy (pronounced demeye) octavo forms, which are slightly smaller than A5. The surveyor ticked off categories to describe type of woodland, approximate age, condition and form of trees, suitability for economic management, and principal species. Our wood was visited on 19th June 1947, and surveyor number 7, with indecipherable initials, divided it into three parts with by far the largest, about 20 acres, allocated to the box with the derogatory term 'devastated'. He went on to assuage the criticism by also marking the box 'suitable' in the categories of economic management. He also recorded the presence of 20–30 year old sycamore and scattered stools of hazel coppice. For the two other stands, one was five acres and marked as felled after 1939 and suitable for economic management, and one was just two acres but had a worthwhile tree crop of 30–40 year old European larch of 'satisfactory' form. This formed a rectangular patch in what is now the larger part of Taid's Wood and close to Railtrack's electrical substation. The total surveyed amounted to only 27 acres and the attached map, a copy of the 1911 edition that was being worked from, shows that what we now call Tanglewood was not included. Also the description of Nain's Copse was not at all accurate, and probably the surveyor hadn't bothered to visit it. So researches showed that immediately after the Second World War most of Northdown Plantation was 'devastated'.

COUNTY					MAP NO.		STAND NO.		AREA : Acres, gross	
HANTS					25 NE		849		8070 20 ac	

SURVEYOR. NO. ITLS. DATE		CODE NO.		CODE NO.		CODE NO.		PRIVATE	✗	
7. J Mm 19/6/47		89		25/2		9		FOR. COM.	2	
NAME OF F.C. FOREST			CODE NO.		COMPT. NO.,		CODE NO.			

	C.H.F.	M.H.F.	B.H.F.	COPP. W.STD.	COPP.	SCRUB	DEVST.	FELLED	LOST
TYPE	1	2	3	4	5	6	✗	8	9
	1/10	11/20	21/30	31/40	41/60	61/80	81/120	OVER 120	UNEVEN
AGE CLASS	1	2	3	4	5	6	7	8	9
	CHEST. COPP.	HAZEL COPP.	OAK COPP.	OTHER COPP.	UNEVEN UND. PL	AGED NT.REG.	BEFORE 8/39	AFTER 8/39	
SUB-TYPE	1	2	3	4	5	6	7	8	
	ELITE FOR SEED	SATIS.	POOR	BAD	STOCK- ING	BADLY OVER- STOCKED	SATIS.	POOR	BAD
TREE FORM	1	2	3	4	1	1	2	3	4
SUITABILITY for ECONOMIC MANAGEMENT	SUIT- ABLE ✗	DOUBT- FUL 2	UNSUIT- ABLE 3						
	S.P.	C.P.	P. CON.	E.L.	J.L.	H.L.	N.S.	S.S.	D.F.
PURE OR PRINCIPAL	1	2	3	4	5	6	7	8	9
	TSUGA	L. CYP.	AB. GR.	AB. PEC.	AB. NOB.	THUYA	OTHER CONIF.		
CONIFERS	1	2	3	4	5	6	7		
	OAK	ASH	BEECH	BIRCH	SPAN. CHEST.	SYCA- MORE	COMM. ALDER	HAZEL	HORN- BEAM
PURE OR PRINCIPAL	1	2	3	4	5	6	7	8	9
	POPLAR	LIME	ELM	WILLOW	NORWAY MAPLE	CHERRY	OTHER B/L		
BROAD- LEAVED	1	2	3	4	5	6	7		
	S.P.	C.P.	P.CON.	E.L.	J.L.	H.L.	N.S.	S.S.	D.F.
SUBSIDIARY (IN MIXT.)	1	2	3	4	5	6	7	8	9
	TSUGA	L. CYP.	AB. GR.	AB. PEC.	AB. NOB.	THUYA	OTHER CONIF.		
CONIFERS	1	2	3	4	5	6	7		
	OAK	ASH	BEECH	BIRCH	SPAN. CHEST.	SYCA- MORE	COMM. ALDER	HAZEL	HORN- BEAM
SUBSIDIARY (IN MIXT.)	1	2	3	4	5	6	7	8	9
	POPLAR	LIME	ELM	WILLOW	NORWAY MAPLE	CHERRY	OTHER B/L		
BROAD- LEAVED	1	2	3	4	5	6	7		

Photocopy of 1947 census record of Northdown Plantation

Our wood wasn't the only one so besmirched. One of the original surveyors remembers an occasion in the early 1950s when the then Minister of Agriculture, Heathcote Amery, visited the Forestry Commission's Alice Holt Research Station and was proudly shown the massive census. He was invited to select any forest stand in the country and, not surprisingly, he pointed to one on his own estate. The surveyor, Mike Locke, looked out the field sheet, from the very ones now archived at Kew and, somewhat disconcerted, read out 'devastated woodland'. Heathcote Amery said he was absolutely right; the stand was sacrificed during the war and he hadn't yet restored it.

'Devastated' in the 1947 census described those stands of trees that had been felled as part of the war effort but now awaited replanting, cleaning or some other operation to bring them back into productive management. Numerous woodlands across Britain were in this condition, like untamed corners of a garden they had been left to their own devices. Indeed, so widespread was the problem that Forestry Commission researchers established elaborate silvicultural experiments to devise ways to cope with the tangle of vegetation, scattered regeneration, undergrowth and other jungle to turn it into a worthwhile tree crop. The owners of the Steventon Estate, the Hutton-Crofts, were mostly interested in shooting and similar country sports and the devastated Northdown Plantation remained neglected. It languished uncared for, became a haven for rabbits, and was only brought into productive use when purchased by the Commission in the early 1950s.

A hundred years before these events the London–Southampton railway line had been constructed. It was a line full of tunnels, cuttings and embankments to ensure the very gentle gradients insisted upon by the underpowered locomotives of the 1840s. It sweeps past our wood at its highest elevation in its entire run, some 393 feet above sea level, and today's trains rush by barely acknowledging incline or descent. But for a time part of the wood was even more intimately linked to the line: in what we now call Taid's Wood there had been a siding. At least this is what Alistair, the former keeper, had claimed and was certainly borne out by the quantities of coal dug up when planting trees in the southern part of the wood in the spring of 1987. However, the Forestry Commission's 1947 survey hadn't commented on this and there was no sign of such a development on the 6" 1911 map. So when did the mysterious sidings exist?

Enquiries led to the happy discovery that one of our friends at church, Roger Bavage, is a railway buff. It says as much on a notice that greets a visitor on entering the Bavage home. And, if more evidence is needed, when he, Christine and their boys visited our wood he identified from distant rumbles the trains that were coming along the line. The very first we heard was, so Roger announced, Virgin Rail's service from Liverpool to Bournemouth that he told us had left Basingstoke at 10.34 am! And a moment later Virgin's wine red coaches hurried by! Roger did later confide that he had checked timetables before coming to know what he might be seeing, but even so, I rest my case. Roger agreed with the signs of a siding once in Taid's Wood and a likely use for unloading coal for Steventon Manor, although the manor is some two miles away by track and lane—there is no village or settlement of any consequence that is nearer. A little later he came up with the first hard proof. In Vic Mitchell and Keith Smith's book *Woking to Southampton*, in Middleton Press's series about Southern Main Lines, Figure 56 shows a fine West Country class steam engine rumbling across Battledown Flyover hauling the empty stock of that day's boat train. This robustly engineered flyover, reminiscent of the Forth Bridge, allows trains from Southampton to join the lines up from Salisbury: indeed, the tracks double from two to four at this point, known as Worting junction, on towards Basingstoke, and is four miles up the track from our wood. But importantly for our enquiry, the detailed caption of Figure 56 concluded with a remark quite unconnected with the illustration. The final sentence reads: 'In the 1930s, there were two sidings for Steventon Manor, on the up side near Waltham Box'. Our wood is beside the site of the old Waltham box—SB for 'signal box' is marked on the 6" map—and it is on the 'up' side and is the one place where ground is level with the track with neither cutting nor embankment. So before the last World War much of Taid's Wood really had been a railway siding.

I wrote to the first named author of *Woking to Southampton*, Dr Vic Mitchell, care of the publishers. Barely a day or two later, my wife learned over the phone that the reference to sidings in the caption to Figure 56 was taken from another source—George Pryer's *Southern railway diagrams* and Dr Mitchell kindly provided an address to follow up. The diagram opposite is the result.

George Pryer, signalling historian, also responded quickly and enthusiastically. The sidings were for Steventon Manor and were laid in Taid's Wood adjacent to the 'up' line. There were two of them, and a gate placed across where it was single line track at a position close to today's 'T' junction of woodland tracks at the bottom. Endearingly rustic and evoking an age of peace, patience and prudence is the note that the key for the gate's padlock was kept in Waltham signal box. Was this for the guard or engine driver about to shunt wagons into the siding, for surely a gate key would be kept by an owner? And, was the box there just for the sidings? The actual length of each siding is also unclear and George Pryer's researches showed that no official publication furnished any details of the traffic handled; it is only speculation that the sidings were used for unloading coal, and the numerous coal fragments in the soil does suggest this was the case. What is not speculation, and all the more amazing for that, is that the sidings were only in place for seven and a half years, and doubtless not even in use all of that time. George's new information raises many new questions, principal of which is why such an investment was made in the first place and why the siding was used for so little time?

The old Steventon Manor is no more. The Victorian mansion, located opposite St Nicholas church, was destroyed by fire and all except the servant's wing is gone. This, and what remained of the old Brocas Manor dating from the fifteenth century, were finally demolished in the early 1970s and the rubble ignominiously used in construction of the M3 motorway some three miles to the southeast. The church still stands and is where Jane Austen's father, Rev. George Austen, was rector and where the novelist worshipped as a child. Sadly, too, the rectory where Jane grew up has also long since disappeared, though for many years after its demise garden flowers would sprout in the field, marking where it once was. Records of Steventon Manor and the estate date back to Saxon times. In their 1000-year history they can boast ownership by both Jane Austen's brother, Edward, who acquired it in 1794 along with

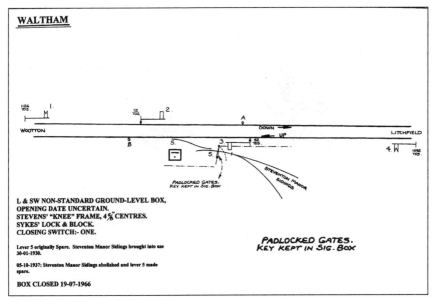

Plan of railway sidings (reproduced by permission, © George Pryer)

other estates as the designated heir of a distant cousin in the Knight family (a surname Edward took for himself from 1812), and by a brother of another of England's notables, author, diarist and pre-eminent forester, John Evelyn. John Evelyn delivered to the fledgling Royal Society in October 1662 its first great discourse, an appeal to the nobility to plant more oaks to relieve 'the impolitic diminution of our timber' which so alarmed the Navy Board (later known to all as 'Evelyn's Silva', first published in 1664). His younger brother, Richard, had a wife, Elizabeth, who had inherited Steventon and other estates along with her sister Anne. She enjoyed a half share, a moiety, for more than 40 years from 1651 to 1692. Whether the great man, John Evelyn himself, visited his sibling's estate is only speculation. His many diaries make no mention of a visit, though he often speaks of dining with his younger brother and his family at Woodcot Park in Surrey. Perhaps matters pastoral and silvicultural of the Steventon estate arose in conversation. More certain is that a century or so later the most famous of all women novelists must have explored its fields, and wandered its tracks and lanes and surely seen the old yew tree at the edge of what we now call Nain's Copse, but was then known as Ashe pightle. Perhaps summoned to view lambing or shearing she may even have sheltered beneath it from heavy showers? No one knows. But we do know that at different times brothers of none other than John Evelyn and Jane Austen once had an interest in the land, Ashe pightle or Nain's Copse, that is now ours. It is humbling.

Some years ago this conjecture led us to name the old prostrate yew in Nain's Copse as Jane Austen's yew. It has been dead for 15 years after blowing down in the great storm of October 1987, but it lies still on the north-western field edge, hardly decaying and demonstrating the astonishing natural durability of yew wood. We called it Jane Austen's yew because she would have seen it dark and evergreen in the distant hedgerow when looking south across the fields from Waltham Lane. It now seems she could have been far more familiar with it, as it was a fair size tree on her brother's estate (farmed by tenants, Jane's friends the Digweeds) and a nice two miles stroll along the tracks and over the downs from her home of 25 years, Steventon rectory. It forms stop 9 on our open day walks.

Here another mistake needs correcting, this time one by a Mr Charles Osborn of Fareham who was the valuer for Ashe parish appointed in 1840 to apportion the total sum agreed to be paid in lieu of tithes. Earlier it was stated that Ashe pightle was owned by Edward Knight and occupied by one Francis William Digby, for that is what the tithe record says. Almost certainly the surname is not 'Digby' but 'Digweed', namely Francis William Digweed. For nearly 100 years, and for much of the time the estate was owned by the Knight family and later by the second Duke of Wellington in the mid-Nineteenth century, the whole of Steventon was farmed by the Digweeds. Not until 1877, when Steventon was sold, did the Digweeds' long tenancy finally cease. What Mr Osborn did not get wrong was the area of Ashe pightle as 4 acres and 19 perches, and he set payment in lieu of tithe at 16 shillings.

Another source of information has been aerial photographs. The initial hope was to find ones dating from the last war that might reveal remnants of the railway sidings, or what devastated woodland looked like from the air, or some other features. Searches led to Cambridge University's enormous collection and showed that many aerial surveys had been done in both the parishes straddled by the wood—Overton and Steventon. Using a map reference, close matches were achieved with archived material only to find that the aerial photography focused on archaeological features not recent woodlands! Nevertheless, within half an hour, several photos dating from the 1960s and 1970s clearly displayed the familiar outline of the wood's hard edges, or at least recognizable parts of it at the top of a photo, or in one corner, or partly hidden by the plane's wing. What was not hidden was the astonishing scenes of crop circles—real ones revealing past subterranean activity not modern subterfuge purporting to be extraterrestrial—showing where iron-age enclosures, settlements, and other imprints of antiquity were. Like giant watermarks in the land, every field that borders our wood, Mike's and Melvyn's fields, the field between us and Bramdown copse, and Upper Ashe Farm's field that jigsaws into Nain's Copse, showed evidence of ancient times and stories long, long forgotten. Our quiet corner of the Hampshire Downs had not always been so.

These researches also explained a confusion. A parish boundary runs through our wood, near the bottom of Nain's Copse, in fact along the exact eastern edge of the old Ashe pightle, and crossing the 19th century intrusion of the railway line just south of Railtrack's electrical substation. To the east is Steventon parish, to the west, containing the bulk of the wood, is the parish of Overton. But that is today's division. For centuries there was a third parish, Ashe, which was long and thin, running almost six miles from Kingsdown to Popham Beacons but often no wider than a few hundred yards. In the middle of the last century Ashe was combined with Overton and the parish disappeared. Nevertheless, in its early years the Northdown part of our wood was largely in the Parish of Ashe. Relating this now communicates poorly the unravelling of local history needed, but it allows us to claim another delightful association with Jane Austen whose favourite niece, Ann Lefroy, was the wife of the Rector of Ashe. Also in this now defunct parish we can report that in the hamlet of South Litchfield, just quarter of a mile along the lane from the wood, a mission-room was erected in the 1880s. Even a handful of cottages were worthy of the gospel as Christ's great commission required. When the building was begun the land that was chosen, in Litchfield Copse on top of Litchfield tunnel, was in fact still the property of London and South Western Railway because they originally thought of excavating a cutting, not tunnelling. Happily the railway company did not persist with objections and leased the land for the mission-room at one shilling a year. Sadly, the mission-room has long gone. I searched for signs of it with Melvyn, the owner of the patch of old beeches atop Litchfield tunnel, where the

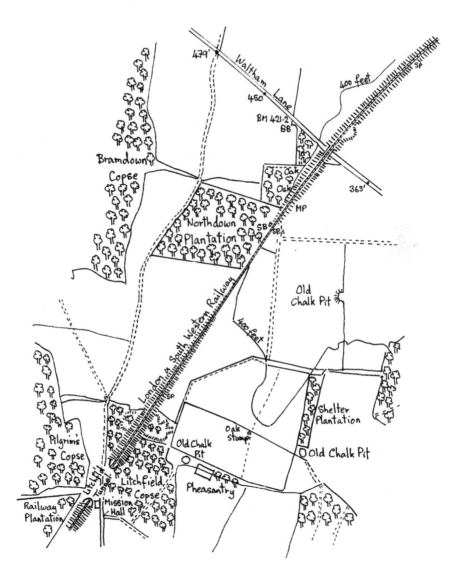

Partial reproduction of 1911 6" Ordnance Survey map

room once existed. All we found was a flat area that would have been suitable, but nothing more.

Between Litchfield Copse and Northdown Plantation is what is left of Upper or Big North Down field. It is now divided among three owners, two of whom I meet regularly. Mike Fisher keeps Northdown Orchard as a thriving organic market garden, and Melvyn—the same who owns the land on top of Litchfield tunnel—keeps just about everything else, provided it dates from before the last war and is useful on the farm. Although his horses are not quite that old, they are useful too and sometimes need special exercising. For this, turning right out of his land and going northwards up the slight incline of the lane by our wood, is his preferred route as I was to discover.

They're a bit frisky

4

Melvyn has worked coppice, mostly hazel coppice, for most of his life. He would journey the lanes of southern England from Chichester to Cheddar plying his trade. In summer his lemon yellow Edwardian caravan with apple green canvas canopy would be parked in high country, as he called it, such as at the crossroads where Waltham and Burley lanes intersect, and in winter somewhere more sheltered and usually well out of sight. More recently Melvyn's travelling has diminished and his caravan less often trundles the lanes and byways of Wessex. He has, too, become a near neighbour, buying the middle third of the field on our southern boundary next to Mike's organic market garden, Northdown Orchard. We have got to know each other a little better and, today, if he sees me at the entrance to our wood, Melvyn will often pull in his voluminous grey van, an elderly petrol driven instead of horse drawn vehicle, and stop to chat.

One morning, leaning on the gate during a coffee break, I hailed Melvyn as usual. He was coming up the lane from the direction of his smallholding and was back in his old caravan with two horses in harness. The lane's width was filled as he came ever closer, the horses pacing a slow clip-clop. No car came along to disturb their progress. Nearer they came, their approach steady and unhurried, almost ponderous, a walking pace making two miles per hour at best. I called out a greeting as they drew level. 'Can't stop!' cried Melvyn 'They're a bit frisky!' An image less frisky was hard to imagine as these two old timers laboured and plodded along the lane. But Melvyn, knowing their temperaments as well as he knows the back lanes from Sussex to Somerset, could tell they were a mite more active than usual and was exercising them. He had no time for coffee that morning.

Melvyn now possesses the water tank that used to stand sentinel where the cross rides in Northdown Plantation intersect the main track. It was one more piece in the jigsaw of development of the land he acquired. His smallholding, called incongruously 'Big Northdown Farm' after the old estate name for the large field of which his holding is just one part, now boasts a substantial barn, a laid hedge of thorn and hazel atop a bank of fulsome primroses, planted trees, free-range chickens with attendant wooden hen houses, equally free-range pigs, a collection of pre-war flour and saw milling machinery, and countless other paraphernalia and traditional gear that together take one back more that half a century. But the 15 acres of 'Big Northdown Farm' also needed the energy that powers the present day, and along with Mike at Northdown Orchard and Railtrack with their substation, he now benefits from a new electricity line. The 33kV line runs overhead to a pole carrying a transformer standing between Melvyn's and Mike's properties. It then runs underground across or rather beneath Mike's land to the southeast corner of the wood and on to the electricity substation beside the railway.

Southern Electric approached us in May 1994 for permission to run an electricity line almost the whole length of Taid's Wood from Mike's land to Railtrack's substation. This was to include erection of a pole at either end, with the one by the substation including a transformer—a grey object that clutches the creosote-tanned pole like an angular koala. They sought an easement for a wayleave, that is the legal right to run a line across our land. They wanted permission to install in perpetuity this provision and opened negotiations. With the legal powers that electricity companies possess we could not really stop their proposal, but we could negotiate whether the cable was carried overhead on poles or buried in a trench. Overhead transmission is much cheaper to install and is naturally the preferred choice, but a line of poles and wires running through woodland extinguishes a swathe of land from tree growing to avoid interference. For even the lowest voltage overland electricity supply, wires must be strung from pole to pole high enough to give minimum clearance—mainly a vehicle consideration—and no vegetation beneath is allowed to grow tall. Such control of vegetation along such a wayleave is maintained to a short distance either side of the line for a width of at least 20 feet or six metres. Arithmetic shows that this swathe width excises from forest production one acre of land for about 660 metres of line length, except for growing small Christmas trees. For us the distance from the boundary with Northdown Orchard to Railtrack's substation was about 328 metres: we stood to lose half and acre or nearly two per cent of the wood. We negotiated for the line to run underground. We insisted that the cable should be buried at least 18 ins deep to avoid any risk of damage from heavy forestry operations and that it should follow the line of the old coaling track that

runs diagonally through Taid's Wood from Northdown Orchard, and then along the main track beside the railway as far as the sub-station. It was almost the shortest possible route, which doubtless pleased Railtrack and Southern Electric, and also gave the easiest possible access for the digger brought in to excavate the trench—which probably pleased them even more. And the woodland's owners were satisfied.

It took nearly a year to sort out. Finally payment came for this easement, calculated as 0.34 p per square metre, based on 328 m x 2m, plus £112 for the poles and overhead equipment. The rate of 0.34 p per square metre is based on annual agreements for such things between the Electricity Supply Industry and the National Farmers Union and Country Landowners Association. The figure for the overhead equipment was derived from an annual wayleave payment for two poles and one stay (£5.60) multiplied by 20 to achieve a commuted payment for not being paid anything ever again. In the end they only erected one pole since the bright red, sheathed cable ran underground across Mike's land as well as through the wood. The easement was added to the legal documents for the wood, doubtless only to surface if ever it is sold.

In October of 1995, we visited the wood with Jean and George from our church and Pam, with her daughter Della. Pam has been our son Ben's piano teacher, and Della the inspiration for the some of the delightful wildlife illustrations in this book, and we found that Southern Electric's digger had begun excavation. We had gone for a picnic to enjoy that autumn's lovely Indian summer in mid October. Nights were still mild and daytime temperatures rose to the low 20s⁰C, perfect for a woodland stroll. In that lovely autumn many a finely woven cobweb was revealed glistening with dew along the hedgerows of southern England. As we reached the diagonal track through Taid's wood, a large JCB suddenly came into sight, silent and immovable, about 30 metres in from Mike's boundary. It obstructed the path, filling the track's entire width. It stood astride, front bucket thrust hard on to the ground and back-acting arm with its head dug into the earth where the trench ended, waiting for new life and renewed excavation after the weekend. It was faintly menacing, an oversize, yellow, rusting, iron intruder, blocking our way as effectively as Shelob in her lair obstructed Tolkein's ring bearer, but without the malice and without the cobwebs.

As chapter 12 later relates, on discovering the presence of the

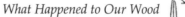

JCB our planned pond was hurriedly laid out there and then with the hope of persuading the digger driver to do a little extra excavation while in the wood. He didn't. The digger was gone by the end of the following week, the cable laid, and the once grassy track a mess of soil, unearthed coal fragments, broken bricks, chalk rubble and other detritus. The trenching job itself was carefully carried out but rain a few days later turned to mud everywhere the track had suffered excavation. Indeed, within a day or two one of Southern Electric's or Railtrack's vans had got into difficulties. Ruts from wheel spin and skid marks from sliding revealed where the driver had slithered, twisted and turned, trying to gain purchase on the now slippery driving surface. November was wet, the bottom track especially became muddy and, for the first time, puddles appeared. The track needed reinstating and I contacted Railtrack, for whom the new electricity supply had been laid, to seek at least a contribution. It seemed opportune to seek agreement from Railtrack to help with maintenance now that the JCB digger had done its work and left its wake of brown like a meandering pass of a single ploughshare.

Railtrack had been granted a right of way through the wood in the 1960s and the legal paperwork appears to make provision for maintenance, but in our first decade of ownership they had not offered it and we had had no sufficient reason to seek it. That had now changed and an estimate was obtained from a local contractor, Norman Goodyear and son, for reinstatement and metalling. It was sent to Railtrack. No reply. Railtrack continued to exercise their right of way, their vans continued to get stuck in the mud from time to time, and they continued to leave other calling cards of their visits. We were no nearer getting support from Railtrack for maintenance.

A dead dog changed everything. In June, after months of fruitless attempts, progress was at last made.

It was during a typical squirrel hopper-checking visit, with my mother along for the ride, when an unkempt looking couple in their early twenties appeared. They said they had been at a party the night before at my neighbours, Mike's, and their black Labrador dog had gone missing and they thought it had been killed on the railway line. It seemed a tall story, but a few minutes later a different Mike turned up, Railtrack's mobile operations assistant from Basingstoke station depot. He confirmed the story; they found the dog dead, still lying on the electrified third rail. He had just come to the wood because a train driver had reported seeing it.

In conversation with this new Mike the matter of the woodland track and its maintenance arose. Apparently I had written to the wrong person, but encouragingly he thought we had a good case. He passed on his mobile number in case of emergency. Only a few weeks later a phone call from Railtrack's Waterloo office said that the proposed sharing of maintenance costs was accepted. A letter with a cheque arrived on 12th August, nearly a year after the original reason for seeking assistance. It was the very day that another phone call came about the wood, the one from a British Transport Police detective related in chapter 1, because a train driver had spotted something else on the line, not a dog, but someone acting suspiciously near Litchfield tunnel.

Track maintenance within the wood has consisted of filling ruts with stone, including raiding railway track ballast where it spills through Railtrack's fence, and importantly clearing the track sides of overhanging hazel. Hazel cutting is needed every few years, and it is a tiresome job. Overgrown hazel has numerous stems that become tangled and when cut they remain hooked together and caught by adjacent stems. Cords and ropes of *Clematis* further ties, knots and entwines with its ever-inquisitive shoots. Often one cuts several stems before the whole conglomeration falls haphazardly, twigs, branches and *Clematis* hopelessly entangled. Hazel never grows taller than 20 or 25 feet and stems rarely become thicker than one's arm so little physical danger attends this clearing back, it is just a nuisance to do. Fortunately my sons and the family of our church's new minister, Clive, Amanda and their son Luke, have helped with either a resigned air or with great relish—you can probably guess which description refers to whom! Opening up the track allows better airflow, and more sunlight and warmth, all of which help keep it dry and less muddy, just like hanging clothes on the line when they dry quickest on a dry, breezy day.

It is constantly a surprise that so many incidents arise from simply owning a small woodland wedged between a lane and railway in the Hampshire downs. Hardly a rural idyll. A few years ago, on the other side of the railway line in a patch of woodland on the left just before the low bridge on Waltham lane, a phone mast suddenly appeared. Like Neptune's trident it rises above the sea of leaves that forms the canopy, proclaiming the era of mobile phones and of instant communication wherever and whenever. It has its uses, since I can just about phone home from the wood, though signal strength is weak, allowing lone working with the chainsaw knowing that, with mobile to hand, contact is possible in an emergency. At the other end of the wood, the field that once displayed a sea of ethereal blue linseed flowers in balmy days of June are now Mike's organic market garden of Northdown Orchard with all its accoutrements, and Melvyn's smallholding, Big Northdown Farm, worked very largely in traditional ways. Two more helpful neighbours couldn't be found, and two more sympathetic, and ecologically friendly land uses are difficult to imagine, yet never again will there be a sea of linseed blue fringing the southern boundary. There are changes, too, along the first part of the journey home from the wood. Two miles from it where the lane joins the A303 trunk road, Popham air field has expanded, a little farther on the Little Chef, with its attendant Esso station, has spawned a counterpart BP station on the other side of the road, and down the first slip-road off to the left, just passed the Forestry Commission's Waltham Trinleys Wood, and still no more than two miles from our wood as the crow flies, is the most surprising development of all.

Miles from the town of Basingstoke, miles from the village of Micheldever and seemingly miles from anywhere, except North Waltham, is Basingstoke's new crematorium. Such a setting for committal of the dead is delightful and evokes the peace of the countryside, but why locate it a full nine miles from the town centre? Is it yet another 'service' carefully sited in anticipation of the day when through persistence a giant insurance company finally gets its way and makes its pile from gaining planning permission for Micheldever new town? They have everything ready, even trees strategically planted on the farmland destined for this urban ingress. A convenient crematorium is one more reason why it should go ahead, it is one more development that could become the death knell of rural north Hampshire. If the new town of 5000 houses goes ahead it will infill and virtually complete the continuous urban sprawl from London to Southampton. Woking, Basingstoke, the new Micheldever, Winchester will soon become just places in a greater suburbia that imprisons southern England. South-east England will become islands of countryside in a matrix of urban sprawl and development. No longer will there be towns and villages in the countryside, but pockets of countryside in suburbia.

The days of rural idyll, of hazel coppicing, of travelling England's lanes, and of exercising one's horses at two miles per hour because they are a bit frisky, are passing. Or maybe this is too sentimental. Only a few miles south of the wood, and in the very same Micheldever, occurred one of the great revolts against change ever witnessed in our countryside. The Swing riots of November 1830 found their greatest expression and greatest repression in the villages of the Dever river valley. Farm labourers rose up against the new threshing machines and, like the luddites, went from farm to farm breaking and smashing them. By so doing, they hoped to keep their manual work. Today we hardly remember the life changing innovations of the early 19th century, rightly called the industrial revolution, so perhaps the changes I lament will be no more than a twist in the skein of time? But one can't help regretting the unremitting infilling of England's green and pleasant land. Yet contrary to this trend of ever more development is the desire by more and more people to seek peace and solitude, to seek what appear to be the certainties and timeless ways of country life. The media knows this, and more and more programmes, both on television and radio, embrace the rustic, the rural and the pastorally romantic. Even our small woodland has not escaped: more than once it has been featured on air.

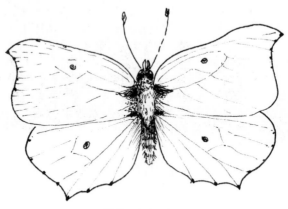

Yellow brimstone

5

From air to air

The first time I saw the wood from the air was from a jumbo jet headed for Miami. Forgive the Americanism, the more so because Miami was only a staging post for onward travel to Caracas, Venezuela. It was on the 16th November 1998, en route to South America for just two days to address a conference of oil people looking at their industry's environmental problems. The topic was forest plantations as a contribution to the energy story and how they help soak up carbon dioxide, which is one of the so-called 'greenhouse gases' that is leading to global warming. As the Boeing 747 headed southwestwards it was adding tons of the offending gas every hour!

I grabbed the view the moment the pilot switched off the fasten seatbelt sign. Seated on the left side of the aircraft the clear view was of Portsmouth, Spithead, and Queen Victoria's beloved Osborne in the Isle of Wight: the wood, being inland, could only be viewed from the other side. The only window available was the small round porthole in the middle of the door to the side of the galley and well forward of the emergency overwing exit. The experienced air traveller will know this description as being business class (a rare experience but just right for so short a visit to South America). Peering out, and there laid out like a map, were the fields and woods of mid-Hampshire sharply etched and clear, on that still frosty, late autumn morning. Directly below was

Alresford—the bright watercress ponds a giveaway—and in mid view was the bronze triangle of the Black Wood of Micheldever with its western edge, straight as any theodolite could lay out, and its beech trees coloured for our English fall! Along this precise boundary runs a bridle path tracing the route of an old Roman road: I had walked its whole length the previous Monday. But on this day, a week later, it was the essential guide, like the pointers of the Great Bear to the Pole star, to search for the wood in the increasingly hazy distant view.

In one of those striking coincidences, a year later Margaret and I were in Hilton, near Pietermaritzburg in South Africa, again because of plantation forestry work. In Tweedie's gift shop, at a new shopping complex, was a pile of A4 sized writing pads and other stationery made from obsolete British Ordnance Survey maps. Casually opening a pad, the reverse of each bright white page was none other than an extract from sheet 185 covering the same Alresford to Black Wood of Micheldever area that was my cartographic guide from the plane. All forty maps in the note pad were cut off a couple of miles short of the wood, just as it seemed that straining and squinting from the plane to see the wood in the distance would also fall short, just beyond my gaze, as we climbed ever higher above the Hampshire countryside.

Still squinting one could just make out the railway line and then, suddenly as if one's eyes come into focus there was the familiar shape, there was the equally bronze and equally beech-dominated wood I knew so well. The line of sight was at a low angle, since the plane was still climbing and still far below its cruising altitude of 35,000 feet, and this distorted the wood's shape. But the stretched 'W', which traces the northern boundary like the stars of Cassiopea, could be discerned atop a square patch of brown. And that was it. I smiled, unsure why, but was content at last to have seen from the air what has been so much a part of my life on the ground.

The strange longing to see the wood from above had been similar to, though stronger than, the wish to see it from the train journeying between Basingstoke and Micheldever or the other way round; a wish not satisfied until August 2001. For my brother-in-law and co-owner of most of the wood, he mostly inspects his investment from the train! It's the first wood on the left after emerging from Litchfield tunnel travelling towards London, that is after the third tunnel to the north of Micheldever station. As the cramping claustrophobic railway cutting gives way to an open view, the wood is glimpsed as the backcloth to a gaggle of plastic greenhouses, assorted buildings, including an all-timber red roofed house of Swedish design, and other gear that comprises Mike Fisher's organic vegetable holding and beside where Melvyn, the coppice craftsmen, has settled. The aerial glimpse was as brief as that from any train, lasting 10 or 15 seconds at most. But it satisfied a yearning and gave cause for reflection in the 9 hours and 33 minutes flight to Miami. Why the smile? It completed the sense of ownership. I've walked the wood hundreds of times. I could point to it on the map, and it is even named on the information-rich large scale OS Explorer series though the cartographers badly fudged the 'W' shape of the northern boundary. Now I have looked down on it. Here was a piece of the jigsaw, just as the map portrayed, for which I was responsible, for which my brother-in-law and I and our wives as owners were the stewards. The wood was there in the geography the map faithfully reproduced, just as it was supposed to be. So it was real after all, from this third dimension too.

These musings were not shared with my fellow passenger, a German visiting Miami, though we did share in complaining to the stewardess that our clotted cream pots were past their sell-by date. They were changed for ones dated 16th November—and so just making it—but several overdue ones turned up in the cabin. So much for Business class! But how judgemental we have become, demanding rights to this and that, expecting the highest of standards, intolerant of the slightest delay and so on. The years of Margaret Thatcher followed by John Major's citizen's charter eroded the sense of duty and integrity to deliver the very best, regardless of the pay or the financial reward. We are encouraged to try hard because it is demanded as of right, not because it is the honourable path. How far our generation has been shifted from the Bible's standard such as found in Paul's letter to the Colossians 3:22–23 '. . . obey your earthly masters in everything and do it, not only when their eye is on you and to win their favour, but with sincerity of heart, and reverence for the Lord.' These musings too were not shared with my German fellow passenger.

On the previous Monday, five of us had walked the length of the theodolite-straight bridle path delimiting the western boundary of the Black Wood of Micheldever. Between me and countryside raconteur, Jeremy Jessel, protruded a large microphone about the size of a wine bottle, though grey and furry and soft not hard, and attached to an extendable pole. Attached to the other end of the pole was Ned, a sound recordist, and a few yards behind him in continuous radio contact and listening to everything was Lucy Lunt, the producer, and her assistant Sally. We were recording the second episode of the Ramblings programme that was subsequently broadcast on BBC Radio 4 at 2.30 pm on Sunday 6th December 1998.

Monday's recording was the second attempt; the first, a few weeks earlier, had to be aborted because of a glitch in the recording gear. The afternoon was clear, the late autumn sun low but glowing, and the air was still, a glorious day after all the rain of that autumn. The idea had arisen when Sally got in touch at the suggestion of a mutual friend, Dick Willan, to enquire whether my walking and forestry credentials would make me suitable as a guest for the programme. It was the second series of Ramblings recordings, and they wanted a forester. Having one who owned a wood appeared to be a bonus. Evidently the credentials passed muster and I was asked to plan a 4–5 mile walk, the ramble, to make the recording.

The walk began outside the church of St. Nicholas in Steventon, famous for being where Jane Austen's father was rector, and

where she worshipped as a child and into her teenage years. After being quizzed on air beyond my competence about the size and age of the churchyard yew by Jeremy Jessel, the presenter, (there wasn't even time to run a tape round the trunk to measure its girth), we set off down the lane towards where the rectory once stood. The building has long gone and all that marks its location is a rusty iron water pump, in a nettle-ridden enclosure of a few yards square, near the corner of an otherwise unremarkable field of pasture. However, we weren't going that way and soon turned left off the lane, climbed a stile, followed a track for a couple of hundred yards then turned westwards along a path beside fields. The whole walk, which began at Steventon, following public foot-paths or lanes, went via the wood, and finished 1½ miles south of the A303 trunk road at the end of the straight bridle path running the length of the Black Wood of Micheldever.

About three hours were spent walking and recording. This filled two hours of tape with forestry and woodland talk, the sound of trudging feet across fields, the snapping and crunching of a wood-land floor, the noise of passing trains, both welcome and not, and of rural song and sound. Talking about trees, woodland crafts and practices for two hours seem daunting, but proved surprisingly easy as Jeremy skilfully elicited facts, comments and observations. Afterwards we felt we had hardly scratched the surface of the rich-ness of forest lore and forest life. But Lucy had plenty of material for a 29 minute broadcast

We entered the wood by a short cut from Waltham Lane through my neighbour's small wood—with permission—and stopped at several points. These had been selected in advance though it quickly became clear that too much material was forthcoming. In the end we only stopped for recording on the northern boundary beneath a crab apple, at the great oak pollard that guards Nain's copse, in the new planting of Taid's Wood, and finally at the entrance gate. When Ramblings was broadcast Lucy had edited out the conversations at all but the first and last of these stops.

There was also an unscheduled stop. My ever present and ever pleasant inquisitor, Jeremy, quite took my breath away and left me momentarily and literally speechless. He had stopped in the middle of Nain's Copse, at a rather untidy bit of it, and remarked what a mess God had made of nature. Possibly he was thinking how tidy man keeps his gardens, but I was at a loss for words. Lucy, hearing everything in her headset was obviously amused, until finally I muttered that Jeremy had got things back to front. Wasn't it more a matter of man messing up what God had made? This exchange didn't survive editing and is only recorded here, and is only my recollection of this wholly unexpected question. Lucy had been careful to ensure that Jeremy and I had not talked much before recording began so that questions or likely points of discussion were not known in advance; everything would be entirely spontaneous and natural conversation. Only once or twice was re-recording needed, such as explaining clearly what coppice was.

One of the stops was at the great pollarded oak that stands at the boundary of Nain's Copse and Northdown Plantation. It's about 230 years old and must have last been pollarded, that is its top cut off some 10 feet above ground and all its branches pruned back to the trunk, something like 100 years ago. Today its enormous uplifted limbs, like thick fingers reaching to grasp the sky, are slowly dying and decaying. Three remain alive, holding aloft crowns of luxuriant foliage. A fourth is dead with bark sloughing off, one fell some years ago but is still precariously propped up at one end unwilling to part from the main trunk, and another must have fallen two or three decades past and lies rotting and chocolate brown in winter but hidden and concealed by dog's mercury in the summer. Gradually this old timer of a tree is falling to pieces. It will take 50 or even 100 years to die. It's too old to attempt rejuvenation like re-pollarding, but this gentle demise is outstanding for wildlife; for fungi, for beetles, for countless micro-organisms, nesting birds, and even for lichens. Every niche and every habitat is utilised, nothing will be wasted. Now the tree is fine and next to it is another almost as sturdy and almost as gnarled, but never pollarded just open grown and perhaps only 180 years old. It will oversee its ageing neighbour's prolonged declension and then take over provision of habitat well into the 22nd century, unlike its present owner.

We walked on from these veterans to young oaks in Taid's Wood planted in 1987 in mixture with ash and cherry. They are growing well and will become maturing oaks during the 21st century and continue the ecological link. The recording walk through Taid's Wood passed occasional piles of discarded dull pink tree shelters that no longer protect their young charges. Some of the tree shelters, of an early Tubex design, had been over-protective, their plastic neither breaking down nor splitting on their own

Hypholoma *fungi*

accord. This failure, owing to too much ultra-violet inhibitor added during manufacture, proved damaging to cherry trees. Their stems were the first to swell and fill the tree shelter, and if not released by slitting and removal of the tube appeared to be 'throttled' as if with a tourniquet. This is an unscientific way of saying that the cherry trees proved most sensitive to such constriction, whereas oak and ash simply squeezed the plastic wider and wider until stretch marks appeared. About a dozen cherries were killed by this plastic throttle, and I was concerned enough to write a short article about it for the Royal Forestry Society's journal *Quarterly Journal of Forestry* to warn of the danger.

Our last stop in the wood, before turning south again along the lane to South Litchfield and on to Micheldever, was at the wooden five-bar gate at the entrance. And here tables were momentarily turned to capture on film this strange sight of radio programme recording. Jeremy asked about public access, the gathering hopes of a right to roam law and related freedoms, and the simple enjoyment of the countryside with which England is so blessed. Northdown Plantation has no public rights of way—there's really nowhere to go—but visitors who go for a stroll are not made unwelcome. They are unlikely to cause harm, there are few hazards, and our public liability insurance ought to cover any unforeseen eventuality. We are neutral about casual public access.

No offensive 'Keep out' or 'Trespassers will be prosecuted' signs are displayed, nor does it say 'Private'. The only change in signage at the entrance has been to remove the name board from the posts that once bore the Forestry Commission's name, logo and access restriction because of sporting rights, and fasten it to the larger of the two gates. It was repainted a chocolate brown, and the lettering was whitened and so underscored the change of ownership from the Forestry Commission and their universal colour of a deep sea green.

The gate also sports a bright solid steel chain just long enough to wrap round twice. Railtrack interlock their padlock with ours at the chain ends to allow either party access. At least this is the idea, but Railtrack don't always comply with the arrangement and from time to time the chain is left loosely locked with only their padlock leaving ours hanging forlornly and uselessly. This seems to happen when, struggle as they might, they can't make the chain quite do two full encirclements. Fortunately Railtrack once gave me a key for their padlock. The new chain was bought following the thinning of the beech and Douglas fir in January 1998 when much mud, much forwarder movement, and much lorry turning at the entrance buried the old rusty chain and locks. Even much searching didn't find it, apart from one of the locks—the one sawn through and which had aroused such police suspicion two years before—and once all the timber had gone the new lock and chain were bought. Alongside the nameboard the bright chain suggests regular use of the entrance gate, care for the wood and an interested owner. The new chain shouldn't get cut as no timber uplifts are expected until the next thinning in the wood in about 2004.

On leaving the wood the recording team turned left along the lane and then left again down the next track but one. At the bottom we bumped into Melvyn; the programme broadcast the meeting as if with a passerby that almost any walk occasions. (The meeting, of course, had been deliberately staged, but it was no less interesting for that.)

Melvyn was splitting, pointing and shaping thatching spars. Sticks of hazel about 28 inches long lay to one side and piles of spars to the other. He wore a leather butcher's apron and, using a kind of trestle for support, fashioned the spars with the skill only time and experience bring. He worked while he talked, unfazed by the paraphernalia of radio interviewing. We watched as he pointed the ends and then with a deft twist, like wringing out a wet cloth, the hazel stick became supple in his strong hands and was bent to create the spar that would peg down thatch. It looked like a giant staple or, perhaps, a croquet hoop, though a little less square. Thousands of such spars are employed in pegging down a single roof of thatch.

The craft of centuries continued before us. The chipping noise delighted Ned and after we had noisily shuffled away and he had recorded our departure, Ned returned to acquire a few more centimetres of tape. He recorded Melvyn at work, and the gurgles of the peculiar pullets—old English chickens—which waddled clumsily around his feet. Egg-laying is more not than often(!), but their fluffy feet and uncertain gait caught the eye and the microphone.

The last part of the walk followed the bridleway beside the Black Wood. It runs straight for a couple of miles and along the equally straight edge of the wood that had been the geographic pointer to Northdown Plantation as the jumbo jet climbed over southern England heading for Miami. We reached the bridleway by crossing the A303 dual carriageway. The finger post clearly indicated that the path crossed this major trunk road though the only acknowledgement of this by the civil engineers was to make the crash barrier in the middle discontinuous where it intersected the line of the now expunged path and so confirm the right of way. What can motorists, rattling past at 70 mph, have thought of this group of five? Away from traffic our talk became desultory, recording only snippets. We were tired, the sun near to setting and a November evening's cold was beginning to penetrate. We finished with coffee and a slightly gooey date slice Margaret had thoughtfully prepared for us. The Ramblings team had sampled this delight on the earlier aborted recording visit and such was their relish that we had to have it again. It is delicious, and the recipe is at the end of the chapter. It is one Margaret acquired from an Australian friend, Gloria Davidson, when we worked in Papua New Guinea in the 1970s.

There, at the bottom end of the Black Wood, ended another Ramblings recording. So concluded this unusual day. It confirmed an interest of many in country things, just as has the evident pleasure of visitors to our woodland open days.

On the return flight from Caracas I made sure of a window seat to glimpse again the wood below. Although there was broken cloud, and the ground beneath was evident, our descent into Gatwick tracked the Hampshire and Sussex coasts and all the peering and straining of eyes could not reveal even a hazy outline of a familiar 30 acres: it was just too far to the north. The final cup of coffee was served, but it was hardly even lukewarm because apparently the pipes, whatever they were, had frozen: so much for a sojourn in club class. Better then, in the remaining minutes of the descent, to ponder whether to have another open day because of the extra publicity 'Ramblings' might awaken. The book wasn't mentioned during all of the recording, and doubtless Lucy would have edited out any reference to it anyway. Even so, we had two open days in 1999.

Marbled white

Margaret Evans' date slice recipe

Ingredients
    4½ oz (125 g) margarine or butter
    6 oz (170 g) soft brown sugar
    1 egg
    1 teaspoon vanilla essence
    8 oz (225 g) plain flour + 1 teaspoon of baking powder
    8 oz (225 g) chopped dates

Mixing
    Melt margarine and sugar in a saucepan. Add dates and remove from heat. Mix egg and vanilla and stir in. Fold in flour and baking powder. Press into shallow tins lined with greaseproof paper.

Baking
    Bake for about 30 min at Gas mark 5 (375°F or 190°C). Near the end of the baking period check that the edges do not burn. Leave to cool in tin and then wrap well in cling film and store in fridge or freezer.

Margaret usually makes a triple quantity in one go and divides the mix between two large 12" x 8½" x 1" tins. If baking on two shelves she suggests that the tins are swapped over half way through. She adds that we like the date slice to be gooey, but baking time can be adjusted to give consistency required.

6

Wildlife glade near stop 6

Open days and awards

Our first open day was held on May bank holiday Monday in 1996. Following publication of *A Wood of Our Own* the previous October, several people enquired if they could actually visit the wood in the story. Perhaps it was a little bit like the desire to see the set where a faithfully reproduced period drama was filmed, or to visit Hardy country in Dorset. But this is a delusion; it was just that quite a few wanted to visit the wood and rather than taking friends round one by one, Margaret and I thought of inviting everyone on the same day.

I had gained plenty of experience of opening woodlands to visitors to display different aspects of forest life and operations. At my former research station of Alice Holt Lodge near Farnham, Surrey, full open days involving every research branch and activity were held about every four years, and subject open days or targeted events almost annually. Whenever the open day included visits to research experiments in the nearby ancient royal forest of Alice Holt, great pains were taken to communicate simply and clearly what was going on. There were usually two alternatives. Either parties of visitors were conducted to each site where a scientist would talk about the research for 10–15 minutes and then they moved on to the next demonstration, or a way-marked trail was laid out with a concisely written presentation board at each stop. This second approach doesn't allow for questions but does permit visitors to come and go as they please and to proceed at their own pace as if in a museum. Until 1996 only the first approach had been used in the wood: small groups of visitors—family, friends, folk from church, professional colleagues—were accompanied to see points of interest, but for the semi-formal open days the second approach was adopted, the way-marked trail, so that visitors could turn up when they pleased on the day in question. In practice the open day is restricted in two ways. First, it is by invitation, albeit spread very widely, and secondly visiting is confined to about four hours with friends coming at any time between 11 in the morning and 3 in the afternoon. This is to allow the essential couple of hours set up time in advance and the hour at the end to dismantle everything after people have gone.

The first open day worked so well that it became the model for all the rest, some six occasions at the time of writing. After parking in herring-bone fashion at the entrance, visitors check in with Margaret at a table a little way down the main track. She gives them a handout of several pages that has a map of the trail, a short description of the wood, a warning about ticks—those tiny blood suckers one barely notices until too late—and the quiz questions which occur at each stop. She gives them a welcoming smile too, as all sorts of guests arrive at wholly unpredictable times in a wholly unfamiliar setting. The trail consists of 12 stops following tracks and paths through Northdown Plantation, Taid's Wood, and Nain's Copse. At each stop a small plaque describes in two or three sentences what one is looking at. Each plaque includes a quiz question for those who enjoy such things. At several of the stops there is something to do as well, though it is Stop 4 that always elicits most interest. It is about firewood, and two small logs of identical size are available for weighing, one is freshly cut and one cut from a seasoned firewood stack that has been drying for 18 months or more. A small spring scale is hung on a crudely fabricated tripod of sticks for the weighing. Typically the newly cut log will weigh about 3 kg, and the identically sized seasoned one about 2 kg. The take home message is that the difference is simply water that has dried off. So when buying firewood in the winter, buy well-seasoned logs, otherwise all one is acquiring is a little wood and a load of water. Not only is this a waste of money, but unseasoned logs don't even burn very well because much heat is used driving off the water that one has paid for: one loses out twice when buying unseasoned firewood.

Erecting the plaques was a teaser. A solid stake was driven home at each stop, but since the plaques were not permanent a heavy-duty wooden or metal base was not called for and the question arose: how were they to be attached? Trial and error led to using a thick grade of artist's card, deep forest green in colour, with the text printed in 24 or 36 point font on white paper. The paper was lightly glued in place and a transparent, sticky, plastic film was delicately unfurled to avoid air bubbles, to seal the face to make shower proof. On the back of the plaque two short parallel cardboard strips were glued in the middle and separated by exactly the width of a mild steel angle bracket. On the flat top of each stake an angle bracket was nailed in place, but its free side had been bent back about 30 degrees to look like an upturned figure 7. This bent strip slid neatly between the two cardboard strips on the back of the plaque. The final step employed nothing more than sellotape to hold the plaque in position by sticking it across the cardboard strips with the metal angle bracket held snugly in between. This is described in detail because, amazingly, such a seemingly flimsy system works even in moderately windy weather, though it doesn't cope well with youngsters tugging at the plaque. I hope it is clear since we have all been frustrated beyond measure trying to follow instructions to fabricate a bit of DIY where the instructions are terse, often obtuse, and clearly a foreign translation.

The plaques, with only minor changes to the text, have survived six open days. They take about an hour to install, necessitating getting to the wood by 9 am on the morning of an open day so that car parking and picnic spot signs, the table, and other paraphernalia are also ready for the first arrivals. The system is satisfactory but there are more robust alternatives to using cardboard plaques stuck with sellotape. The solar eclipse of 11th August 1999 led to one such possibility.

Margaret and I were spending a few days in Cambridge at the time of the eclipse—only our youngest son had set off to Cornwall hoping to see it in totality. We decided to witness this astronomical phenomenon in the solitude of the most ancient of Britain's nature reserves, the National Trust's Wicken Fen. We arrived about an

in aid of REHAB

Saturday 3rd July 1999
11am - 3pm

Come and enjoy a day in the woods.
On a guided trail learn about trees,
test your knowledge, or just listen
to the birds.... ....and it's not just any old woodland...

⇨ Featured on BBC Radio 4 Ramblings
(6 Dec. 98)
⇨ Subject of book: "A Wood of Our Own"
Oxford University Press
⇨ Received Forestry Commission Centre
of Excellence Award in 1996

**The wood is between Basingstoke and Micheldever
2 miles north of the A303. Take lane from North
Waltham to Overton, turn left at the second crossroads
and look for the REHAB sign.**

Map ref. SU533 473 (OS Sheet 185)

For more information contact Margaret Evans

hour-and-a-half before totality, predicted at about 97 per cent where we were, and were mildly interested to discover if birds would fall silent, though as is well known August is the poorest of all months for birdsong. We changed into walking boots—a fen is wet underfoot—and then picked up a trail guide from the small visitor centre and set out along the medium length 3.6 km nature trail advertised as taking 1¼ hours. At about the fourth or fifth stop, near the wind pump, the obvious suddenly became the apparent: each stop communicated its message of nature or nurture not with a plaque or display panel but by numbers relating to the text in the trail guide. This system is widely used, so might it be suitable for Northdown Plantation open days? The attraction is that the text can be changed with ease and the route modified simply by relocating the numbered posts. There was time to ponder; our next open day was not until 1st May 2000.

The eclipse itself was mysterious and deeply impressive: breathtaking, yes, but more so. The first hint of it—we hadn't dared look up—was seeing two women well ahead of us on the trail standing motionless staring at a puddle left from overnight showers. They were some way off, statuesque, two muses with heads inclined, and expression intent. Coming close they beckoned, whispered, and pointed to the sun's orb, already obscured across a third of its face, perfectly reflected in the puddle. We joined them like Brer Rabbit's 'friends' to behold the golden disc floating on the surface. Unlike Brer Rabbit's friends we didn't trawl through the water to catch the shimmering reflection. We too stood still, hushed before the unfolding phenomenon. After a little while we walked on alone and, from time to time, glanced into the full dykes to see in the safety of a reflection the sun's face gradually eclipse by the moon's ingress as the heavenly bodies inexorably converged in their celestial paths. A few minutes before totality we sat down on a bench thoughtfully placed under an elderly, wizened silver birch overlooking the great dyke called Wicken lode. All fell calm, the wind too stilling and pausing in its hurry for the precious passing of the cosmic wonder. We waited for totality, occasionally viewing the sun in the lode, the gloom gathering, and listening to the birds. Time passed slowly, pausing too in awe. Idly I began to fiddle with the binoculars and then tried projecting the eclipsing sun onto a sheet of paper. Suddenly it, or rather they, since binoculars have twin sets of lenses, flicked into view. A little focusing and a lot of steadying of hands produced sharp images, and by my holding the instrument and Margaret the paper at a few feet distance, a large view was provided. Thus we observed the solar eclipse— along with a few other visitors to the fen who gathered round to view the event displayed by our rudimentary projection system.

The birds didn't fall silent though it became quite cold for about a quarter of an hour as the flow of energy that bathes and blesses the earth was intercepted by its moon. And we didn't in the end adopt Wicken fen's trail marking system of numbers and guide booklet, but the precious day made us thoughtful.

At each stop on an open day trail, the scene is described in short sentences. How old the trees are and of what kind. What the next job is that needs doing, or why the bark is scarred owing the grey squirrel damage. One plaque tells the story of the great oak pollard at the corner of Nain's Copse, another relates the attempts to construct a pond in our waterless wood. In these ways the life of a woodland is conveyed, a working woodland that changes with the years and with the seasons, yielding profit and pleasure, wilderness and wildlife in the only way a wood uniquely can. In essence, we display our stewardship of this small corner of God's creation.

So far all the open days have been by invitation. Each time about 150 friends, professional colleagues, relatives, folk from church and Tearfund and any others who have expressed interest, are invited. To our delight between 60 and 90 have responded on each occasion with only one exception. Visitors may stay only long enough to enjoy a quick hoof round the trail or they make an outing of the visit bringing a picnic or to play games.

The level of interest encouraged us, since usually open days are on a bank holiday Monday, such as the two possible in May, or a Saturday. There are many alternative attractions on such days and going to a 30 acre wood can't be high on most people's list. The one

Jane Austen's yew, inspected by John White, at stop 9

exception to the generally good turnouts was in July 1999 when the Saturday set aside coincided with the women's tennis final at Wimbledon and only 30 or so came along. This was a pity since the open day was a deliberate fund raising opportunity for Rehab, the charity which has so helped Margaret's recovery from a heart attack. And, even of the 30, one couple came thinking it was a place for 'pick your own' strawberries! They hold the record for speed in completing the trail, doubtless disappointed and dismissive of the uncollectably tiny but deliciously sweet wild relatives of what they were seeking. The wood abounds in wild strawberries. The couple had lost their way and seen our open day sign: they were gone within half an hour.

The second open day remains the most memorable. At midday a Centre of Excellence award was conferred by the then Forestry Authority of England. Alan Betts, the regional conservator, presented the award, a robust weatherproof plaque erected at the wood's cross rides, and a framed certificate. In addition a photograph of the great pollarded oak adorns our sideboard as the third mark of successful recipients of such awards. The inscription says 'for combining forestry and conservation'. The scheme only ran for five years from 1992 to 1996, but raised the profile of forest stewardship. Though now discontinued, there are many other awards and prizes that woodlands can receive.

Like a farmer entering a fine bull at an agricultural show, it is possible to enter a stand of trees or even a whole forest for an array of different prizes. Unlike the farmer taking his animal to be judged in the arena, judges visit the wood and inspect it in the weeks leading up to the occasion the award is made. The best known is run by the Royal Forestry Society of England and Wales. Each year they advertise the categories of woodland or stands of trees to be judged and which counties are eligible. Thus one can enter stands from one's forests or woodlands roughly once every five years, assuming of course they are considered worthy of entry. Judges are severe critics, looking for quality of stem, spacing of tree, development of crown, and countless other evidences of competent tree management—of good silviculture in forester's parlance.

Apart from the Centre of Excellence award, we have only entered parts of the wood for two competitions. John, my brother-in-law and co-owner, submitted it at the New Forest show in 1997—it was commended and criticised! I entered the young, but well-grown trees of the new planting of Taid's Wood into a TGA (Timber Growers Association) competition for stands established in tree shelters. Tree shelters are the plastic tubes, usually pale pink or sometimes green, that litter our countryside, but have proved a boon for planting small groups of native trees like oak and ash. They were the invention of Graham Tuley, a fellow researcher, in the late 1970s and for years were known as 'Tuley tubes'. The shelter or tube protects the tender seedling from browsing by rabbits and deer, allows easy control of weeds around it, provides a greenhouse environment to help early growth, and actually shows where the tree is! It is remarkably hard to find a little oak or ash to release from amongst dense herbage and all too often such newly planted trees suffered 'Sheffield Blight', that is they were decapitated along with cutting weeds by a worker wielding a scythe. Tree shelters have proved a blessing in many situations. Certainly the trees in Taid's Wood, which we planted in 1987, have grown well, though apparently not well enough even to make third place in the TGA's competition! Perhaps failure to prune and clean the plantation quite when it was needed was to blame.

The New Forest judges' criticism was that the beech trees, already 40 years old, and which make up most of Northdown Plantation, were growing too tightly. They needed thinning out. It struck home, and within six months a substantial selective thinning was in full swing as chapter 8 relates. The thinning was needed, and certainly in my mother's view hastened the change from beech plantation to maturing woodland. The more open conditions, the longer views, and the dappled rather than continuous shade displayed the wood in a more favourable light, figuratively and literally. John was also taken with the improvement and urged that we resubmit it for the New Forest show. This we did in 2000.

For its second judgement, the woodland was entered for the Meyrick cup. A fee of £25 accompanied the forms and a few weeks later Graham Darrah and Chris Oliver, the judges, were shown around the wood. The thinning worked and the wood was awarded the prize, but doubtless meeting the judges helped as we could tell them our vision for the wood, why we left wildlife glades, what the dead wood piles were doing and so on. It was self indulgent, but fun nevertheless. Later in the year, a hot dry Friday in July found all four owners, John and Gill, and Margaret and me, in the members' enclosure of the New Forest show ground located in the heart of the New Forest. After seeing more cattle and livestock imaginable the time for awards came, and for our minute of glory. John kept the certificate and I thought we were going to provide a home for the cup itself, but it never came. What did appear that day, in the sense that was when we first saw it, was a finely crafted crop circle beside Alresford bypass. It looked like a many petalled flower well laid out but not of cup-winning standard.

Woodland competitions are one aspect of a much wider enjoyment of a living classroom foresters rely on to learn their craft. Farmers who meet weekly or monthly at livestock sales can share the ups and downs of the business—far more downs in these uncertain times—but foresters resort to organised visits to one anothers' woods. Many organisations, including the two already mentioned, arrange several meetings a year where forest stands are inspected, the quality of trees assessed, the emerging requirements of woodland certification aired, and grants and taxation issues mulled over as one inspects the professional handiwork of a colleague. We view the stand of trees before us, hear the remarks about growth and yield or silvicultural desiderata, and then like art critics pass comment, offer advice, or give praise to the hapless owner or forester whose responsibility it is. Although colleagues are invariably generous and helpful, having one's woods examined in this way is a bit like a driving test where you notice far more acutely than usual what is rather second rate or what job ought to have been attended to. But the experience of visiting and being visited is a fine forestry education.

For Northdown Plantation and Nain's Copse the one recent occasion for a professional visit was in late June 2001, and it was as an experiment. The Southern division of the Royal Forestry Society wished to try out an evening meeting of about two hours duration, in contrast to the normal whole day affairs. June 27th was selected and Whittaker's almanack consulted to show sunset almost at its latest possible at 9.26 pm. Members were scheduled to arrive at 7.15 for 7.30 pm thus giving about two hours, which is just right for conducting a party around the 30 acres, a fine summer's evening assumed—or at least prayed for!

Many members came, more than 60 including guests, and 25 or so cars were shoe-horned into the entrance area and Mike's overflow space. The high summer evening's sun illuminated the main ride and, summoned by a rasping electric megaphone, we set off in the time-honoured crocodile. Lady Colman, the society's regional chair, presided over the affairs, and I as the owner and manager introduced technical topics at each stop. The usual open day route was followed, but time would only allow five stops knowing the penchant for discussion and forestry talk. Questions were raised about beech regeneration, about whether to retain a few of the fine Douglas firs, now close to rotation age and final felling, when and how to thin the promising young crop of hardwoods in Taid's wood, and what to do with the unusual mix of ash, sycamore and oak in Nain's copse. In Nain's copse its history and former use as a pightle was described by Gerry Dutton, the local historian who was so helpful in uncovering the evidence and, in the party, was Mrs Church from whose family we had bought this unusual additional wood in 1994. Several local foresters, keepers, and neighbouring landowners came as well as others from farther afield. It was an honour that so many turned out, and a pleasure to see Alistair again, the keeper who practised his craft in the wood in the days when we were only lessors. The evening was a success in that two hours of worthwhile forestry debate and evaluation were enjoyed, all the more so since Dr John Jackson, the society's

Greater spotted wood pecker

director, had come all the way from Tring in Hertfordshire to see how things went. I hope the wood too passed this very public exam.

The exam it didn't pass, the criticism of the New Forest show judges in 1997, directly spurred the action chapter 8 relates. Before that it bears repeating how the responses to our open days, indeed to visits generally, have been a surprise and a delight, a giving and receiving of pleasure. But one such response will forever be special because of events that were to unfold.

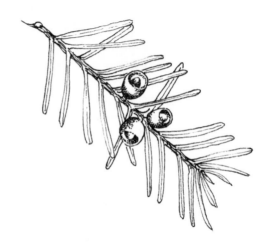

7

Are you sitting down?

'Are you sitting down?' were Ina's first words when she rang to tell us the verdict. Margaret, my wife, and I were walking by reception in the d'Ouwe Werf hotel in Stellenbosch on the way to dinner, and the phone had rung. On hearing the receptionist say 'Professor Evans' we exchanged glances, the call was for us. We had wondered whether to phone ourselves, but thought better of it thinking it was still too early to expect our son back in England to have e-mailed Ina in South Africa's Cape Town with the news. We had been staying with Brian and Ina Hamilton and had kept in nightly touch by way of this remarkable internet facility. That evening, now 40 miles away in a hotel, we had decided to wait until after dinner and then make the fateful, old-fashioned phone call. But it wasn't to be, we were intercepted, like some pre-ordained rendezvous timed to the nearest second. As we rounded the receptionist's desk on our way towards the vine draped patio that led to the restaurant, the call came. And Ina's first words were: 'Are you sitting down?'

All year the clouds had been gathering. A close friend, who had been a church youth group leader, had been arrested, charged with sexual assault and then released on bail. I felt we were all on trial as the police pursued their investigations, taking statements and building a case. The accusations dated back some years, and what quickly becomes apparent is the near impossibility of proving innocence against such a claim wholly devoid of outside witnesses or forensic evidence. Like returning from some fantastic trip, without photos or video or even postcards, who is going to believe how close the pride of lions really were in the game reserve, or that you really did bungee jump down the Victoria Falls gorge? Such was the case of our dear friend. It seemed unbelievable from all we knew about him. We had known the family well for nearly 10 years, everything argued that the accusations were baseless and entirely out of character. But how do you prove this?

Slowly the due process of the law took its ponderous course. Three times appearances in magistrates' courts moved the proceedings forward and brought ever nearer the seeming inevitability: our friend would have to stand trial. The charges were reduced, but were never dropped by the Crown Prosecution Service. And, three times not a word of this 'scandal' was scented by the press. Apart from the awfulness of what a guilty verdict would mean to our friend and his gracious wife and family of four, the other fear was that the matter would be picked over by the press with all their delight in finding the immoral and criminal in the very body claiming the moral high ground: the church. We've all read the reports and reflected on the contradictions when such have been reported; was another sorry chapter about to be added and bringing the name of the Lord Jesus Christ into disrepute?

Words cannot describe the feelings of shame, of bewilderment, and simply of pain surrounding these events. Even now they evoke memories perhaps best forgotten if it wasn't for the school of experience and testing that God allows us to pass through. I relate all this, as a brief interruption in the story of the wood, because the family involved was one who had helped with work in the wood, who had visited the wood just after we thinned the oaks in Nain's Copse, and who after coming to an open day had sent us the loveliest thank-you letters we have ever received from their four girls, perfectly reflecting their four different feelings about our wood at their different ages of 11, 8, 6 and 5 years! The eldest's poem I now reproduce, with her permission.

Are you sitting down?

Sing a song of Springtime

Sing a song of Springtime
Where the dewdrops line the grass,
Where the sun shines through the treetops,
And the shy brown rabbits pass.

Sing a song of Springtime,
Where the violets peep through,
And the primrose rules the woodland,
With the bluebells ringing true.

Sing a song of Springtime,
Where the carthorses have trod,
The forests silent, now as then,
And I'm at peace with God.

Lindsay
May 1996

Lindsay's poem is reproduced because of its personal association, its delightful childlike but not childish picture of our humble wood, and because she is the bravest of young ladies. Entirely on her own initiative she wrote to her father's solicitors and told them that daddy was innocent because she knew that at least one thing was wrong in what had been claimed in the appalling accusations. And she was prepared, young as she was, to stand up in court and say so. And stand up in court she did as a witness for her dad. Many, many witnesses spoke up for our friend, but none as young and perhaps none as brave as Lindsay.

These memories are still fresh, being written only a few days after the fateful call relaying to us the outcome of the trial. They are written in the tranquil surroundings of the colonial style Ramalea guesthouse overlooking the green hills of the Hans Merensky estate of Westfalia that bedeck the gentle slopes of South Africa's Drakensberg mountains just north of Tzaneen. A place of greater solitude or greater peace is hard to imagine. A greater contrast to three weeks before of waiting outside court is hard to imagine too. I wrote down this account of our feelings and emotions 6000 miles away from where the drama unfolded with the blessedness of objectivity that distance can bring.

And so Ina had said: 'Are you sitting down?' We had left England not knowing the outcome. The trial had been at the summing up stage, with the jury not yet retired to consider their verdict. Thus every scrap of information we gleaned from Stephen's emails was welcomed. We were much in prayer and so were our friends, Brian and Ina.

Lindsay's poem has been one of many wholly unsolicited expressions of appreciation after visits to the wood. It seems that a visit is more than just looking around, more than just marvelling at the soft, almost tangible green of beech trees in spring or their golden and russet tints in autumn, more than just the freshness of air or the dampness, muddy yet clean, which is so much purer and quite unlike the dirty rain of city streets. These are experienced, absorbed like the charm of a much loved melody playing almost unnoticed but instilling peace and well-being; and yet there is more. Special interest is found in interpreting what one is seeing, why the trees are as they are, how the wood came about, what impact the railway has had and so on. Setting the woodland visit in the context of its history adds the fourth dimension of time to the very three dimensional and impressive experience large trees already afford. It all led to the semi-formal open days described earlier.

Not every letter nor note of every phone call has been kept, but the above remarks capture the kinds of responses visitors pass on to us. Kept, of course, are the pieces about Northdown Plantation that have appeared in the press. Twice Duff Hart-Davis has visited the wood, and twice he has 'done us proud' with an item about us or the wood, or usually both, in the following Saturday's *Independent* newspaper. For the tidy minded the dates are Saturday 30 May 1995 and Saturday 28 June 1997. One other mention occurred in the *Daily Telegraph*, but I knew nothing about it until a friend at church asked me about the piece. He was as mystified by my reaction as I was trying to fathom what he was on about. The writer had referred to *A Wood of Our Own* and cited my name, but it was news to me.

The wood's profile has also been raised in semi-technical articles. When in the mid-1990s the Forestry Commission downsized I applied for the opportunity to go early, very early in fact at age 50. Among the new opportunities to open up was writing for *Country Smallholding*, a monthly magazine for hobby farmers, smallholder enthusiasts and others with an interest in rural life and rural goings-on. It has an astonishing circulation of 22,000, not so far short of the well-known and up-market *Country Life,* and clearly taps into a rich vein of interest. The editor invited an article about owning and buying a wood in November 1997. Forty articles later, all on tree and woodland themes, the magazine's Contents page lists me as their regular woodland contributor!

Most articles draw heavily on experience with Northdown Plantation and Nain's Copse. Indeed without our own 'smallholder forestry' I couldn't have spoken from the heart. How else can one genuinely communicate practices and operations, pitfalls and problems, and everything else to do with anything from a small patch of trees to a substantial block of woodland? The monthly challenge was deciding a theme, writing in a clear unambiguous style for the practitioner to follow, and offering the publishers suitable illustrations to choose from. Probably one-third of the photographs used were from the wood, so in addition to John White's sketches in these pages snapshots in colour can be found in many of the issues of *Country Smallholding* since late 1997.

The richest, and much the most professional colour illustrations, appeared in *Country Life Gardens* in Summer 2000 and were shot by *Sunday Times* photographer Peter Baistow. Richness was not only in colour, but also in choice of subject, as only an artistic professional of his calibre would see. I admire our wood for its trees, Peter saw in them pattern and patina, foliage and form, the beautiful and the bizarre and captured it in celluloid. My job was to provide the supporting text.

The wood has featured regularly in one other way, in the quarterly newspaper of the Timber Growers Association, called the *Woodland Owner,* which appears as an insert in their magazine *The Timber Grower.* The *Woodland Owner* began in 1997 as part of an initiative to recruit owners of small woods like ours who needed help with technical information and management advice. Britain is full of small neglected woodlands and the Timber Growers Association, along with bodies like the Small Woods Association, want to do their bit to improve things. Writing features in each issue of *Woodland Owner* inevitably drew on experience from the wood, but even greater care has to be taken than with *Country Smallholding* since my efforts have to get passed the Woodland Initiative's director, Judith Webb, who owns her own small wood and excoriates any flannel.

It was because of other writing about trees and forests that we were in Stellenbosch in the western Cape of South Africa. We were there to begin organising a conference about what is termed 'social forestry', that is where growing and caring for trees provides benefits such as fuel, poles, shade and shelter, fodder for animals and so on which are so much needed in tropical countries. They are, too, just the sorts of benefits trees that small woodlands can bring even in temperate countries like England though the extent of such interest reflected in the *Country Smallholding* articles and other media contacts has been a surprise. We were staying at the historic d'Ouwe Werf hotel, the oldest existing inn in South Africa dating back to 1802, having been captivated by its charms three years before when in South Africa to lecture as a Hans Merensky fellow. The hotel is not only the oldest existing inn, but is on the site of where the first Christian church in Africa south of the equator was built in 1687. The remains can still be seen beneath the present day kitchen. Obviously, north of the equator, Christendom in Egypt or Ethiopia for example pre-dates it by more than one and a half millennia, but in darkest Africa here began the first worship of the Christian God.

We didn't sit down to take Ina's call. But we did hear Ina read out the e-mail from Stephen saying that our friend had been found not guilty of any of the charges. The jury had retired to consider their verdict just as the court rose for lunch. By the time lunch was over and the court would normally resume proceedings, not only had the jury doubtless devoured their sandwiches but they had remarkably quickly made up their minds that the verdict was 'not guilty'. For dinner, we did sit down to relish a meal that only such news could make replete.

As the previous chapter records, I had been subjected to an infinitely less serious trial. A very different verdict on a very different subject had been reached by a panel of two judges on the state of the beech stands in Northdown plantation. Inspecting them as an entrant for a New Forest show prize their summing up was that the beech trees were underthinned! There was no defence, I was guilty of neglect. I, who had written the Forestry Commission's textbook on how to care for trees, known in forestry circles as Bulletin 62 or *Silviculture of Broadleaved Woodland,* and which included an entire chapter on how to grow beech trees properly, was found guilty. The thickly stocked trees were witnesses against me, and, professionally, I was upset at the comments from the judging, and accepted the sentence. The beech must be thinned.

8

Thinning the beech

The beech stands that make up most of the wood did need thinning. In 1997 they were 40 years old, having been planted in 1957, and had never been thinned properly though they had been opened up and given more growing space. Before we bought Northdown Plantation in 1985 the Forestry Commission had line thinned the pine trees, removing one out of three rows, and so opened up conditions to the side of the one of the three rows of beech. The 1957 planting had striped the wood with alternating belts of three rows of pine and three rows of beech. Also, just after we bought the wood, we had carried out a 'firewood' thinning of both the beech and the pine and removed the most misshapen, diseased, weak and unwanted specimens. Moreover in 1992 all the pines had been felled, which greatly opened up space around the remaining beech and, in a sense, had been a very heavy thinning for them. But it was true, there had been no selective thinning among the beech trees to favour the best and remove the worst, nor had they been opened up much within their three row strips. The judges considered these shortcomings as jobs that needed doing.

In a selective thinning, indeed in most kinds of thinning,

between one-quarter and one-third of the trees are removed each time. What is special about the selective approach is that each tree to be cut out is chosen and marked for removal individually. It is the opposite to a mechanical thinning, like line thinning, where simply every row is cut out or every third tree, or some other systematic operation which takes no account of tree quality. Selective thinning allows one to consider each tree and so remove the worst and favour the best. For broadleaved trees, like our beech (but equally true of oak, ash, wild cherry, sycamore and other broadleaves) it is important to commence selective thinning as soon as possible since so few trees have reasonably straight stems, or well-shaped crowns, or are free from defects. If the good ones are not identified and favoured early on they are easily overtopped by the ungainly, poor quality neighbours that foresters call 'wolf' trees. As thinning succeeds thinning the stand of remaining trees gets better and better just like a ranger culling a herd of deer to improve it. He only selects the weak or sickly specimens or ones ill-suited to herd society so that the rest are healthy, have space and don't exceed the carrying capacity of land. Of course, unlike deer our beech trees don't move around. But as they grow older the best are left and given progressively more space in which to grow. And also unlike deer culling, there are fewer and fewer of them as they get bigger and bigger until only the final crop of the very best remains. One may start out with 3000 or even 5000 beech trees in a hectare of forest and end up with only 100 to 150 trees, after as many years of their long rotation. Selective thinning ensures that it is only the best that make it all the way.

Within weeks of the judges' uncomplimentary remarks, we decided to proceed with a thinning and to proceed quickly. Rather than first select and mark the trees for removal and then offer them to market, a rough estimate was made of the likely quantity available and a small ad placed in the July issue of the trade magazine *Woodlots*: the ad included the fact that the parcel was a third thinning of 40-year-old beech. *Woodlots*, developed and funded by the Forestry Commission in the early 1990s, puts buyers and sellers into contact: it is the *Exchange and Mart* of the industry and tends to attract the same end of the market! But I have never been disappointed on the five occasions that timber from the wood has been advertised in it, and the advertising is free. The ad for the beech thinning appeared on the 9th August and on a hot dry day a week later some 1300 trees were selected for removal using fluorescent pink spray paint specially manufactured for marking trees. Spot marks were squirted on the lower easterly side of the trees so as not to be visible from the lane at the top and not too obvious as one walked down the main track. But looking back up the gentle slope, it seemed that the wood had caught measles! As the paint dried it brightened by magnitudes. Spotted trees were scattered through the woodland as far as the eye could see; a rash of spotted-tree disease! At least the tree fellers could easily find the ones to cut in the dimmest and dullest of conditions. All was therefore ready for buyers to inspect.

The actual process of deciding which trees to award a pink spot for cutting, took one very long day. Working systematically along each three-row wide beech strip, poor and misshapen trees were first marked, and then ones that interfered with the best stems. This is a tiring job, continually looking up to see if a tree is badly forked or appears chlorotic with pale foliage, or to check that a specimen which looks fine from one side is still so on the other. The neck begins to ache as the day wears on and the countless, but irrevocably final decisions of trees to mark for felling become more casual. The white marks dabbed on many of the best trees some 10 years before when doing the firewood thinning were a help. The old marks were still visible. However, every so often two or three good trees would be growing close together and a new decision was whether to fell any of them. Usually such groups need not be broken up since beech trees are able to grow well together, even to maturity as a pair or triplet, provided the group has space on at least two sides. Indeed, some German research into thinning beech confirmed these empirical observations and commended just this approach: for beech, always choose the best quality stems and ignore whether they are well spaced out or not. It was a day of decisions, a day of squirting pink paint on trees condemned for felling. Only after the trees had been felled would the look of the stands tell if the thinning had been 'about right', but of course by then it would be far too late to do anything about it. It must be a bit like choosing lottery numbers on the ticket—an experience I've never had—in that once chosen the numbers are fixed for that week's draw. For the beech, though, you can't try again the next week!

Marketing had preceded marking because smallish beech trees were not selling well since their main outlet, apart from the erratic demand for wintertime firewood, was pulpwood. The one mill, at

Sudbrook in Gloucestershire, which pulped such wood to make the corrugated fluting of corrugated cardboard, was erratic in its requirements. At times the mill would receive deliveries at other times it would not. So there was no certainty that the parcel of beech thinnings would prove attractive. Added to this a selective thinning is a more costly way of harvesting since each marked tree has to be picked out individually and felled rather than working mechanically along a row. As with all fellings of any quantity in the wood, the trees were sold where they grew: a process known as 'standing sale'. The buyer pays for the trees in the wood and is responsible for felling, trimming, and extracting them as well as selling on the logs or hauling them to market. It means that as the seller, the offer one gets is the profit one makes, after notionally deducting the small cost of marking them. But would this measly parcel of beech even find one buyer?

As well as interest from our neighbour Melvyn, the coppice worker, three enquiries arrived asking for more details as a result of the *Woodlots* ad. They came from well-known forestry companies, one of which was based only five miles from where we lived. On 20th August I hastened to the wood to improve the estimate of how much timber was for sale. Five randomly located sample plots were laid down to estimate the average diameter of the 1377 pink spotted trees. The diameter of a tree is measured on the trunk at an internationally agreed height above ground that rejoices in the name 'diameter at breast height' or DBH for short. This is 1.3 m above ground, or 4ft 3in, except in the USA, where everything has to be bigger and better, and is set at 4ft 6in! The estimated average DBH of the beech trees turned out to be 14.6 cm or about 6 in across. The total quantity of wood on offer amounted to about 125 tons. These estimates were added to other particulars sent off in response to the enquiries including the location of Northdown Plantation, the good access to and within the wood, how trees were marked for felling—ones with the shocking pink spots—when felling was to be done, that a single payment was required up front, and that offers should be submitted no later than the 19th September. As these details were sent off, my notes record that an offer of £1000 was the hope but realistically £500 likely to be nearer the mark. However, even this is optimistic, since as we had learned with selling Corsican pine trees in 1990, an enquiry is one thing, a firm offer quite another. For most of September it was a question of simply waiting and hoping.

The way of estimating how much beech timber was on offer described here is unconventional and, while open and honest, relied on the 'buyer beware' principle. Most parcels of trees of any size are measured for timber volume using a procedure devised in the 1950s by the Forestry Commission's research arm. Conventions have been agreed between industry, sellers and buyers, and by adhering to them a reasonable estimate is obtained. Reasonable means an estimate that statistically is within 15 per cent of the actual volume. It is easy to count trees for sale, a little harder to determine their average diameter, and much harder still to calculate the volume or tonnage of wood; trees are awkward shapes. The method devised, know as the Tariff system, systematically samples the trees to be felled to obtain an average diameter or DBH. A sub-sample of these is actually cut down and, being on the ground, the trees are easily measured for their volume from their cross-section diameter at the mid-point between the bottom of the stem and where it gets too small to be worthwhile, usually when it narrows to 7 cm. A relationship is worked out between the volume and the DBH of each sample tree and used to assign a tariff number from a look-up table. The average tariff number of all the felled sample trees is applied to all the trees and the volume of the whole parcel calculated. I had used this procedure when selling 630 tons of pines in 1990, but the beech on offer in 1997 was a much smaller parcel and was a much less valuable commodity, only expected to attract about one-third of the price per ton. Thus the unconventional but simpler and much quicker system was used. This fact was made explicit in the particulars.

Two offers arrived by the late September deadline. Powell Forestry offered about £5 per ton or about 50p per tree. This was a fair price, but it makes the point that an entire beech tree that has grown for 40 years and is perhaps 50 or 60 feet tall is worth no more than a daily paper. Not much to show for the passing of the years! But they were thinnings and were the poorer trees only fit for the indignity of pulping.

A contract was drawn up and sent off to Powell Forestry in early October. Such contracts are much like any other transaction and conveyed the ownership of all the trees with pink spots. In under a fortnight full payment was received, and not only for the trees. Alan Powell bought all the unused spray cans of shocking pink too! The income was shared with my brother-in-law, thus completing the transaction, or so we thought.

Powell Forestry began to fell the trees they now owned in our wood in mid December. A felling gang of three got to work and made the most of every minute of precious daylight in the few hours available to them for safe working. Within a week I received a phone call. It was from Alan himself, and it went a bit like this. Since the men were in the wood, and all the gear and equipment there—a modern forwarder tractor with its grapple had or was about to arrive—could they also cut the scattered groups of Douglas fir trees that were among the beech? This would make Powell Forestry's operation more efficient owing to economies of scale and obviously bring in a bit more for us and probably at a good price since the contractor was already on site. The catch was that none of the Douglas firs had been marked and I had only the roughest ideas of the volume involved. There were four groups of these firs, two patches at the top and two near the bottom of the wood. Alan was particularly keen to cut the ones at the top to help open up access to the beech. This was a fair request since the larger area of the Douglas firs at the top was where it had substituted for the rows of pine elsewhere in the wood and had never been thinned beyond a cleaning for firewood. Cutting the Douglas, as foresters would say, would be the key to doing a good selective thinning of the beech. Without doing so it is questionable whether the forwarder could have gained access to all the marked beech trees. Such were the thoughts as we talked on the phone, and naturally Alan wanted a quick response since they would only be in the wood for another week or two at most.

It was agreed that Alan could cut all the Douglas at the top of the wood where the trees were intimately mixed with the beech, but only to take thinnings from the two sizable clumps at the bottom near Taid's wood. The Douglas at the top were getting a bit chlorotic because of our chalky soils, one or two had dead tops, but they would make a worthwhile extra parcel containing a reasonable proportion of logs as well as smaller rails and other produce. He was asked to leave two big ones near the entrance to remind us of the crop that had been there and because gold crests, with their high-pitched squeaks, found such conifers congenial. We agreed a price for these extra trees that included the thinnings at the bottom even though they weren't yet marked! This latter job was done the very next day, and 42 Douglas firs singled out for thinning. The Douglas were much bigger than the beech, and though far fewer in number, were much more valuable. Their total volume remains a

guess, but they probably sold for about three times the price per cubic metre of the beech thinnings. I was satisfied, and Powell Forestry obviously were—their second cheque arrived in two days despite being sent by second class post in the middle of the Christmas rush!

Normally one cannot throw in extra trees at whim for a contractor to buy, like a street vendor sweetening up a customer, because this would transgress the explicit conditions of the felling licence. In this case, however, the thought of including a heavy thinning of the Douglas was made when applying to the Forestry Commission for the licence, but afterwards it had been decided against in order to keep the two operations, the thinning of the beech and thinning of the Douglas, separate. It was good that this did not happen. Taking the Douglas at the top resulted in a good, albeit belated thinning of the beech, and today it is difficult to see where they had once been. The thinning of the two patches of Douglas at the bottom has created attractive stands ready for a final felling in a few years time. They may even be thrown in when next thinning the beech trees to spice up the sale since doubtless the beech will still be a low value product.

The team of contractors employed by Powell Forestry, Gwyn's Timber Contracting, travelled each day from the Forest of Dean. The journey must have been an hour-and-a-half each way though at the time of the winter solstice it was one way of using the darkness that so curtails the working day outdoors. The three-man gang worked conscientiously. Felling was tidy, few branches were torn from the remaining trees, there was little bark abrasion, and lop and top was trimmed down to tolerable piles. They were finished at the end of the second week in January just as the Brunet forwarder arrived to gather up what the fellers had cut and left stacked in neat piles throughout the wood.

The forwarder was an eight wheeled vehicle, which gives low ground pressure and so does little damage to the soil, and had a hydraulic grapple for picking up logs and loading them on to a giant cradle attached at the back. It was frame steered, that is it was hinged in the middle of the chassis rather than being steered by its front wheels like a car, which confers great manoeuvrability. It is ideal for working in the confines of a wood with the obstacle of trees scattered everywhere. It completed its task of lifting, fetching, carting, and unloading logs by the entrance gate in a few days of work, though it was in the wood for several weeks, being in need of repairs on two occasions. By mid-January much of the produce was at the gate and the main track was muddy owing to persistent rain while the forwarder had driven back and forth. And the mud didn't stay in the wood. Twice on visiting Northdown Plantation the lorries that had come to haul pulpwood to Gloucester or Douglas fir logs to a sawmill had deposited great droppings of mud in the lane. Mike Fisher, our neighbour, twice used his tractor to drag free badly mired lorries: such is the peril of mid-winter woodland work in the wet. I only learned later of this kind act of good neighbourliness. My own contribution on two different days was to shovel away mud layered thick and clogging the narrow lane. By the end of February all was finished, the logs were nearly gone, and any remaining mud weathering away. It will be about eight years before such activity disturbs again either soil or solitude.

Mud wasn't the lorries' only hallmark. In one of their manoeuvrings where the bell-mouth entrance opens onto the narrow lane, difficulties were encountered. The already frail fence on the south side was shattered. It was probably so weak that the driver didn't even notice reversing into it, but it left us an important repair to do. Untidiness and uncared-for conditions attract rubbish and waste and general dumping, and we had had our share.

Thinning the beech uncovered a surprise, a bit of the wood's recent history. More than three-quarters of all the freshly cut

stumps left by the thinning showed black rings and occluded bark at about number 17 and again at 26 rings counting in from the edge, i.e. 17 and 26 years ago. Around this damage subsequent growth was often vigorous and distorted showing rapid callusing of the wound like one sees when a pruned branch stub heals over. In some cases the scarring almost encircled the stem. It is the calling card of past attacks by grey squirrels or rabbits. Both animals damage trees severely by stripping or peeling bark. Seventeen years ago took us back to the winter of 1981/82 which was cold with snow lying on the ground for some weeks, just the conditions for hungry rabbits to gnaw bark. The older damage may also be by rabbits. Certainly when we bought the wood in 1985 it was heaving with the endearing lagomorphs, though more recently we have suffered the attentions of grey squirrels. Although the proportion of trees damaged was high also a surprise was that none appeared to suffer any decay or even staining of the timber. Thus similar damage, which must surely have happened to the remaining trees as well, shouldn't have harmed the timber. I write this in case someone buying the final beech crop in 70 or 80 years is reading these words and is fearful of what might be inside what should be fine high quality trees!

Further inspection of the rings showed that the beech had grown very slowly as young trees. Narrow rings indicated very slow thickening of the stem. Although this is a feature of beech, did browsing of foliage by rabbits and perhaps by roe deer, as well as vigorous competition from the pine trees they were planted with and from woody weeds such as clematis, briers and sallow, all combine to make the beech struggle to get established? Probably so, but now they are the main crop and the challenge is to care for them as well as possible, to shape them into the best crop they can achieve. Apart from further thinnings and protecting from damage, only one tool is left to do this, but it is a powerful one and one that deserves a chapter to itself—pruning, the way foresters do it.

The beech trees have been thinned, and so have the Douglas firs. And as my mother remarked on a visit soon after, it has opened up the wood and turned it from plantation into woodland. No greater compliment could be paid, the thinning must have been about right. It was time then to help the very best trees achieve their potential. A final pruning for them couldn't and shouldn't be delayed. No longer delayed either, is an account of the wood's profitability, which comes first in the narrative since the beech thinning is the last significant source of income before this book is published, and to dispose of the questions about the wood's income that are so often raised.

Beech leaves and nuts

9

Has the wood made money?

I am often asked: Has owning the wood been financially worth-while? It is, after all, unlike many investments since the final cut of a tree crop—the time when significant income can be expected—is when trees are 40 or 50 years old in case of most conifers, and any-thing up to 150 years for broadleaves. The longest rotations, as these ages are called, are for such very common trees as oak and beech. Investing in woodland by buying bare ground and beginning a plantation incurs a very long wait indeed for a return and that is one reason why tree planting is subsidised by grants from government that typically cover about half the cost of the operation. That was very much our experience when planting the four acres of Taid's Wood in 1987. In this chapter the income since 1985 is summarised along with relevant expenditure—'relevant' because much expendi-ture on the wood has not been necessary for its essential manage-ment, but made out of choice. A formal balance sheet isn't presented because determining profitability was never a primary objective, detailed records of every single expenditure have not been kept, and because some of the figures quoted are necessarily estimates.

There is a dichotomy, a tension, at the heart of this chapter. For me the wood is a hobby, an engaging and enjoyable one, and for a hobby like gardening or sport like golf one neither costs one's time nor thinks whether it is economically worthwhile. It is simply enjoyed. But for my brother-in-law and his wife the wood, or at

least the Northdown Plantation part we share 50:50, is an investment that figures somewhere in their pension planning. So the
same woodland fulfils these two roles. Bearing this in mind I'll try
to answer the question in the chapter's title. Clearly what isn't fair
is to set against the investment all the visits I make and all the
things I do for pleasure alone. Here I have provided details of the
timber we have sold and the price received per cubic metre or, in
one instance, per hoppus foot! This is probably what most enquir-
ers really wanted to know, namely, what did you get for the pulpwood, how much did the heavy thinning of pine go for, and did
the reasonably good oak logs make a reasonably good price? I
think that is what is meant by: 'Has the wood made any money?'

Before starting, there is one other issue to consider. The 22 acres
of Northdown Plantation were bought in 1985 for £9100, but as a
leasehold property. Neither sporting rights nor immediate use of
four of the 22 acres of woodland beside the railway were available.
These details influenced the price but are now incidentals, since
the freehold has been acquired, and sporting can be let or not if we
wish, and the four acres are now in hand. Also we have purchased
an adjoining 7½ acres. This all makes the point that in forestry as in
farming there are two elements to profitability. First, there is
income and expenditure from the tree crop itself, that is the business of growing trees; secondly, there is the capital value of the
land on which the trees stand, that is woodland as an asset which
may vary independently from the trees themselves. It is not always
easy to separate these in one's thinking because only at very long
intervals can one ever consider changing the type of tree crop. A
farmer can switch his crop every year, a forester is lucky to be able
to do so once in half a century.

Starting with the second aspect—the wood as an asset—it cost,
as already noted, £9100 in 1985. In 1994 the much smaller adjoining
wood, most of which is Nain's Copse, was bought for £10,000.
However, this price included acquisition of the freehold over all 22
acres of Northdown Plantation as well. In effect, though not spelt
out as such in the 1994 transaction, £8000 was paid for the freehold
of Nain's Copse, or just over £1000 per acre which is a typical
figure for maturing broadleaved woodland in southern England,
and £2000, or just less than £100 per acre, for acquiring the freehold
over Northdown Plantation. Thus, today, we have as freehold 29½
acres of woodland or 12 hectares, and it cost in all £19,100. Strictly,
for determining profitability or return on investment, adding

together 1985 sums of money to 1994 ones and presenting them as a total in 2002 is incorrect, since inflation has intervened and greatly changed the value of each pound. This is what bedevils forestry economics and, indeed, any investment with very long time spans. Here I will duck the issue and simply indicate the kinds of amounts in the years they were received.

An interesting question now is to ask how much the whole wood is worth today if put on the market? Two people were approached for a valuation: John Newcomb who was the agent who sold us the wood in the first place and also advised on the subsequent purchase of Nain's Copse, and Colin Gee of John Clegg and Company who specialise in selling woodlands. John Newcomb's estimate was made at the end of 1998 (when I was first thinking about this chapter) and, much more recently, Colin's in early autumn 2001 when this book was nearly finished. Thus it's no surprise that their figures differ: John's 1998 estimate was £35,000 and Colin's more recent valuation an unexpected £50,000. So, our asset has appreciated; it is obviously more valuable now in cash terms than when we bought, and even in real terms it has appreciated about 1.8% per annum. This satisfactory result probably flows from the combined affect of enlargement and the acquisition of freehold.

Colin's valuation, thanks to the helpfulness of Cleggs, is revealing. His letter, like estate agent's particulars, touches on the key issues in assessing a woodland. The tree crop itself is noted, the species present and their age, but so is the good internal access within the wood and the equally good access externally, namely frontage on to a public road. The diversity of trees and stands is seen as a selling point—it makes it a delightful wood, but I am biased—though as for the selling point of proximity to London I am less sure! That said, the fact that the M3 and A303 roads are within three miles is a plus to allow quick and easy visits and for marketing timber.

So what of income and expenditure for the wood that we've owned for 17 years? What have we earned and what has it cost to manage? Here the picture is more complicated for two reasons. There have been many costs, both small and large, for doing an array of different things, and they have been incurred in many different years. To find out what the trees as a crop have done to date, woodland operations are divided into two. First, there is activity that directly earns income such as marking and selling trees and,

John Clegg & C⁰

RURAL SURVEYORS
VALUERS & CONSULTANTS

Our Ref CMG/AA

16 October, 2001

Professor Julian Evans OBE

Dear Sir

NORTHDOWN PLANTATION, NR BASINGSTOKE, HAMPSHIRE

In accordance with your instructions we have visited your woodland to enable us to provide you with our opinion of the current Open Market Value. The woodland is well known to you and so we will not describe it in detail.

We understand the whole property including Nain's Copse amounts to 30 acres (12 hectares). It has frontage to a public road on its western boundary and a gated entrance. We believe the property is freehold and that the shooting rights and mineral rights owned and are not let.

Apart from two small areas of Douglas fir the woodland contains broadleaves with beech planted in 1957 predominating. This has been well thinned following the removal of the Corsican pine and should develop into a valuable crop. There is 4 acres of oak and cherry planted in 1987 and 8 acres of ash and sycamore coppice with oak standards and mixed broadleaves including birch, hazel, wholebeam, field maple and hawthorn.

The combination of well grown beech plantations and the variety of the other deciduous species make this an interesting woodland. The well presented ride system permits the crops be easily viewed and appreciated. This property is well located and easily reached from the M3. It is under 60 miles from central London and would be popular with prospective purchasers looking for a woodland for investment, capital appreciation, Inheritance Tax saving, sporting, leisure or merely for quiet enjoyment.

Assuming the property is freehold, of good title and free from onerous restrictions we believe the current Open Market Value is in the order of £50,000 (fifty thousand pounds).

Yours faithfully

John Clegg-lo.

JOHN CLEGG & CO

The Old Coach House, Southern Road, Thame, Oxfordshire OX9 2ED. Tel: 01844 215800 Fax: 01844 215252
E-mail: woods@johnclegg.co.uk Web site: www.johnclegg.co.uk

J E Clegg, BSc, FRICS; A N Crow, FRICS; G R Watt, BSc, BLitt, CDipAF, FICFor; J F Welstead, BSc, FICFor; J M Lambert, ARICS
J A Clegg, FRICS; C M Gee, FRICS; C A Hughes, NDF, MICFor

Scotland: John Clegg & Co., 2 Rutland Square, Edinburgh EH1 2AS. Tel: 0131 229 8800 Fax: 0131 229 4827
Wales: John Clegg & Co., Apex House, Wonastow Road, Monmouth, Monmouthshire, NP25 5JB. Tel: 01600 715311 Fax: 01600 714234

secondly, there are general management tasks that cost time and money simply to look after a wood properly. The latter, in terms of estimating expenditure, is the more problematic owing to the continuum from essential, through desirable, to simply out of choice. I regret now not properly maintaining a complete and distinct set of woodland accounts, but I hope to provide enough here for a judgement to be reached about the wood's profitability.

So far there have been five main receipts of income from the trees, four of which were planned. The fifth, the unplanned one, came from insurance after the battering of storms for 10 days in late January 1990 and was not very satisfactory, though it must still feature to complete the picture. Minor income has come from firewood, sale of wood for turning, payment for granting an easement, and a contribution to track maintenance. Also forthcoming have been small but welcome sums of grant aid from the Forestry Commission. Besides the revenue, there are the directly associated costs of bringing timber to market which are given if known or shown mainly in terms of my time connected with making each sale, so as to get close to what a farmer would call his gross margin. It led to the amount that was shared equally with my brother-in-law for any produce coming from Northdown plantation.

The first sale was a firewood thinning in 1985/86 when about 200 tons of poor quality thinnings were sold. I say 'about' since no formal volume estimate was made, but I remember haggling at prices, in those rosy and long-gone days, of around £4 or £5 per ton (today one would be fortunate to get the work done at no cost). The buyer, Smallwood Services, undertook all the felling, extracting, log-splitting, and marketing of trees that had been blazed and so was entitled to cut. They were mostly overgrown hazel, poorly shaped beech and a few redundant pines. Blazing small trees with a hand axe is time consuming, raising blisters and depressing returns if it has to be paid for, more especially for such a low value commodity as firewood. For this reason the job of selecting which trees to cut is usually left to the merchant or contractor, a practice called 'worker select', with the owner or manager simply checking from time to time that it is being done fairly and that only the poorest trees are taken. However, I was keen to mark the thinning as a way of getting to know the then newly acquired wood, and in total the job probably amounted to an extravagant three working days. The quite good price we got may have reflected that all the marking had already been done.

By far the largest income came when all the pines from among the rows of beech trees were sold. Originally Northdown Plantation was an alternating three row:three row mixture of beech and Corsican pine. The Forestry Commission had line thinned one of the three rows of pine, leaving us a plantation consisting of three rows of beech and two of pine, like the frieze on chapter 2, when we acquired the wood in 1985. Most of the firewood thinning was among the beech, but the storms of 1990 revealed the vulnerability of the pines, and the decision was taken to fell them all. This produced an estimate of more than 600 cubic metres and the parcel was sold standing to Mendip Forestry in July 1990. They offered a figure typical at the time for maturing pines with a moderate sawlog content in the region of £13 per cubic metre. Marking and measuring the trees using the Forestry Commission's tariff system took a whole day and other work, such as applying for a felling licence, drawing up sale particulars and other administrative tasks, about another day.

The matter about the insurance is appropriate here since it immediately preceded the sale of the pines. Although only eight trees were blown down in the great storm of October 1987, we were less fortunate in the January gales of 1990 when 114 trees were uprooted and a few others snapped off. Many of them were the largest and most impressive pines and totalled about 45 cubic metres and getting on for one-tenth of the whole pine crop. When the insurance paperwork went in it transpired that we were liable for the first £1000 of each and every claim! Since the total estimated loss of timber and cost of clearance came to £1393 only £393 was forthcoming and of that at least £200 had been notionally spent in measuring the mess of fallen trees and submitting an estimate. At best the compensation in terms of income was £193. A higher

insurance premium might have covered us for all losses, but we had simply accepted the standards terms.

The next income came from selling 43 mature oaks and one ash from a heavy thinning among standards in overstocked coppice in the autumn of 1994. The average volume of the trees was a little less than two cubic metres. They were not sold standing but presented felled and trimmed, 'at stump' as it is called. And, as those in the trade would suspect, the volume for sale was not advertised in metric units, but in the time and tested measure dating back to the 18th century of 'hoppus feet[1]'. Because more work was done, and done by others, preparing the logs for sale is easier to cost. The fee for arranging the sale was £300 and the cost of felling the trees, trimming and presenting the logs, and cutting and cording the branches for firewood was £900. My time for marking and measuring the 44 trees amounted to not quite a whole day. In hoppus feet units, the felling operations cost 25p per h.ft and the offer accepted for the reasonable quality logs was £2.25 per h.ft.

The most recent income in 1997, as related in the previous chapter, came from thinning the beech and cutting some Douglas firs. Thinning the beech yielded less than £5 per ton as pulpwood, i.e. not even 50 pence per tree, while the larger sized and much more attractive Douglas firs probably earned three or four times the amount per cubic metre. As explained in the previous chapter the firs were added to the parcel late in the day and I did not measure their volume accurately. The thinning method used was the most expensive though most beneficial silviculturally—selection thinning—and in all took me about day and a half armed with a spray can emitting colour, if not music, to match the Pink Panther, to seal the fate of the rejected.

Finally, we have received various small sums for firewood sales, for wood for turning, and a few Christmas tree tops from Douglas fir thinnings that over the years amounts to only a few hundred pounds in total.

Each of the main felling operations made a net profit, though the best one was from the pines in the early 1990s. Adding up the

[1]Hoppus foot is a measure of volume named after Edwin Hoppus a surveyor of the City of London in the 18th century. He devised the unit for measuring timber to avoid the frauds perpetrated by others. He decided to set pi (π) as 4 and thus make the volume estimated for the contents of a log to come to fewer cubic feet than true cubic feet. It allows for losses when cutting off the sides of a round log to make a square baulk. All quality hardwood logs such as oak, ash, chestnut, sycamore and cherry are still measured and still sold in hoppus feet. One hoppus foot (h.ft) = 1.273 cubic feet. There are 27.7 h.ft in one cubic metre.

revenue received over the last 17 years and bearing in mind that forestry was taken out of the tax environment by the Chancellor's budget day announcement on 15th March 1988, the narrow-sense profit has been satisfactory. It is narrow-sense in that money made from each sale is only that. For the woodland as a whole there has been much other expenditure on management. The essential operations are as follows, each figure representing an estimated *annual* cost (2002 money):

	£
Insurance premium	40
Repairs and maintenance of gate and track	100
Protection, mainly grey squirrels	300
Silvicultural operations—pruning etc.	200
Total	640
Less grants received	(1350)
(£270 for 5 years, 1992–1997)	
Less contribution to track maintenance	(350)

Over 17 years of ownership the estimated essential expenditure comes to a net £9180.

Protection costs should diminish in the future since the main crop of beech is growing out of the stage most vulnerable to squirrel damage. However, there will be no more maintenance grants either, since the wood is now considered to be able to generate regular revenue. As for revenue itself, the outlook is bleak. Over the next 20 years there will be two more thinnings of beech, another 60 cubic metres of Douglas fir, that together may earn £4000, and then perhaps in 20 or 30 years time a few more mature oak and ash may be ready for cutting. None of the present owners will be around when the beech trees of Northdown Plantation reach maturity. That is perhaps 70 or 80 years away, though they are wonderful to enjoy now as they grow.

What the revenue picture really reveals is that the most profitable part of the crop has already been realised, the Corsican pine trees felled in the early 1990s. There remains now the long years of growing as the main beech crop develops and slowly matures, but as just remarked there are countless other ways beyond the financial to enjoy and share the wood.

Taid's Wood, consisting of the ash, oak and wild cherry planted in 1987, will soon be thinned, an operation which at best can only be expected to cover its costs. The balance sheet of actual expenditure and grants received from the Forestry Commission can be summarised by saying that the grants covered all the cash expenditure of buying plants, tree shelters, weed control equipment and herbicide spent in the first few years, but left nothing for the labour. John, my brother-in-law and I, gave our time for planting and I think we both enjoyed the task and 'enjoyed' the blisters back in 1987, so we can call that fun, essential though the task was. Since then there have been regular weedings in the first few years and, more recently, a return to a task I began my forestry career with— cleaning.

So has the wood made money? And what about collateral income such as from the book about the wood, *A Wood of Our Own*, this one, and articles in *Country Smallholding* magazine? They, of course, are not strictly part of the wood's accounts and have been wholly unexpected developments, though welcome nevertheless. For Margaret and me, owning a woodland hasn't primarily been about the money, more a rich vein among the many strata that build one's life layer upon layer: rich in experience, in new relationships, in learning of country ways, in writing about it and sharing it. God who is rich towards us all, has blessed us with this patch for a few decades to care for. And we want to pass it on in good heart. But the honest answer to the chapter's title is that we are quite satisfied with what this rich vein has yielded.

There is one job that will improve just a little the prospects of the beech, and other trees, in many decades time. Indeed for our children's children to gain from. It is a job that should have been finished by now, namely to complete the high pruning of the best stems so that as they are favoured in thinnings over the years they become the finest specimens they can be. It is a favourite task of some foresters, with no certainty of better returns. It will never do harm, and is great exercise for the pruner—the person, not the saw!

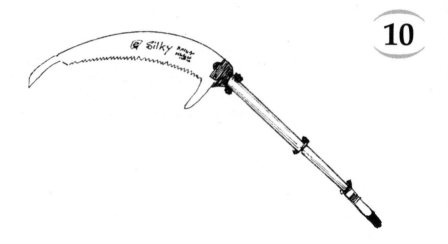

10

Pruning for pleasure and profit

Sweat stung the eyes and branches blurred. Beneath the beech trees there was no stirring of a cooling breeze. The canopy of green allowed only an occasional sun fleck to penetrate and not a breath of the suffocatingly humid air to escape. Though a glorious morning, the heat wave of August 1998 was taking its toll. On most Saturdays and several weekdays, high pruning of the beech trees, newly released after the previous winter's thinning, proceeded apace. It was a good time to prune, both because in summer wound infection is scarce and the scar dries quickly, and because after a thinning trees are making the most of the extra space in which to grow. But it was too hot. While not every day reached the tropical 28–30°C achieved in the middle of the month, every day in the wood was warm, and each time the exertion of pruning made sweat pour, and each time tiny rivulets of salt-laden perspiration trickled into my upturned face and eyes. Screwing them shut to staunch the pain, sawing had to stop, and forehead and temples wiped dry. The handkerchief was soon soaked like a flannel, but the stinging subsided, and with sight restored sawing off the branch resumed and then on to the next tree. With each visit to the wood 20 or 30 trees were pruned before time, tiredness and temperature took their toll and labours ceased.

In the last five years all the best beech have been high pruned. When we first bought Northdown Plantation the lower portions of selected stems were pruned, but in the last few years a final lift has produced long clear boles on the finest trees. Since the pruning saw can reach over 20 feet and by adding my own 5ft 8in plus a bit more with arms outstretched, branches up to about 27 feet were within reach. This final pruning mostly removed side branches from about 20 feet up to this ultimate height. It's higher than foresters usually go, but should eventually create a fine stand.

I like pruning because it is helping make the very best of a tree. Branches are carefully sawn through almost flush with the stem, not absolutely flush but just proud of the bark creases known as the 'branch bark ridge'. The cut is slightly angled working away from the trunk to avoid cutting into tissue of the main stem. Doing it this way helps limit risk of infection by fungal diseases. Once the wound heals, and the trunk once again has a continuous covering of bark, all subsequent wood is free of the knot that the branch would have made. Provided the job is done soon enough, typically during the first third of a tree's intended life or rotation, then a worthwhile layer of high value knot-free clear wood is produced. Like pruning roses to create the best blooms, or the vine to develop handsome bunches of plump grapes, high pruning trees concentrates the best of new wood on the best of trees.

I like pruning for another reason. It helps defeat grey squirrels. They are lazy creatures when it comes to stripping bark and prefer doing it sitting down. Most bark is chipped or peeled off a tree either at ground level or in the crutch where branch meets stem where the wretched animal sits comfortably cradled as it tears off then discards flake after flake of bark. Prune away its perch and damage is less likely. Also, piling pruned branches around the base of a tree, to look like the nests of the mythical Pegasus, adds an obstacle course that helps deter squirrels. Though I sweat as I prune, the exercise is good, denying squirrels an easy peeling is even better, and the higher quality beech and sycamore trees may be best of all for revenue in the future: I can relish the first two of these fruits of pruning. It's worth the sweat.

Reaching to prune above 20 feet is tricky. Like drawing out a car aerial to its maximum, all four lengths of the light aluminium saw need to be extended. As each length slides out it is clipped into place and secured by a red plastic lever that tightens the grip like a seat belt buckle. It's a cleverly designed and remarkably robust telescopic pruning saw, designed by a Japanese manufacturer, but as each length is added it gets just a little more unwieldy. Fully extended it is certainly usable but requires skill and concentration. The art is to move from tree to tree keeping the saw still erect as if marching on parade with a flag. Allowing it to fall is not only dangerous for the saw but 20 feet of pole puts dangerous leverage strain on the operator's back. Nevertheless, this piece of far eastern inventiveness whetted the appetite for high pruning.

The pruning action itself is also tricky because at 20 feet or more it is that much more difficult to see, sweat or no sweat. Like dusting the cobwebs in the topmost recess of the stairwell one can't always see what one is doing or what obstacles are obscured from view. And, like dusting the farthest corners, one gets tired craning the neck looking ever upwards. The pruning saw is slightly curved and its teeth sharpened to cut on the downward or pulling stroke, the upward push or thrust mainly helps clear sawdust from the cut itself. The knack is to keep the cutting angle and saw alignment absolutely constant otherwise at 20 feet distant on the end of a flexing pole the blade jumps about, starting numerous little cuts like a child's first clumsy attempts with a toy saw. The best way to develop such a remote cut is not to rely on arm movement but to hold them steady and, instead, move the whole torso up and down by bending the knees in a series of mini squat thrusts. Holding the arms steady helps hold steady the saw's position. Once the cut is a deep groove, arm action can take over.

For most branches, four or five saw strokes suffice. The exception is of course a thick branch, but also cutting out (singling) a fork usually takes more effort. The limbs of a fork slope steeply upwards and cutting is more with the grain than across it, and the saw's teeth are not well designed for what is really a ripping rather than cutting action. It's the same with tearing cloth, easy in one direction more difficult in another. As the cut progresses the branch will almost imperceptibly start to move, and then begin to bend down a little, at which point it is time to adjust position, first for a moment to cut more vertically to minimize tearing of bark when the limb is finally severed and then to retreat and cut at an angle as the branch begins to fall more quickly. This takes time to describe, but with practice becomes second nature and is done in a trice. With experience one is soon adept at making little adjustments.

One lesson learned early on is that even small branches falling from 20 feet are dangerous. While rarely being hit, wearing a hard hat just in case is an essential precaution. Wearing gloves is another matter. With them on, the hands are also protected but they impair one's feel. Even though cutting is at the far end of a long high pruner the feel of the cutting action, the stiffness or pinching of the cut are all transmitted to the hands and help in gauging what is happening. A second lesson learnt is not to stand downwind from the saw. As it cuts sawdust rains down like fine snow and because, inevitably, one looks up specks and not only sweat get in the eyes. But sweat is the main impediment. The humidity beneath the beeches is amplified inside the enclosed space of the orange safety helmet almost bereft of breather holes. The sauna the scalp experiences soon raises a sweat, sun or no sun, hot or not so hot, and wiping of the eyes is frequent as the little beads trickle down. But despite everything I like pruning.

From time to time branches don't behave predictably and the saw blade gets pinched. This is less frequent with the Japanese silky pruner than with my old saw, but still occurs. On one occasion during the hot August of 1998 a large beech branch was nearly severed and began its downward bend as the cut deepened and then it stopped completely, held up by a small beech tree in the understorey. It rested just past horizontal, enough to begin a split at the cut end as it unhinged from the tree but not enough to complete the separation and open the cut. The pruning saw's blade was gripped like a vice as the leverage of the long branch pinned it against the tree. All the usual solutions of waggling the saw from side to side, deliberately working it backwards and forwards like a pendulum, or giving it an extra hard tug down or a vigorous push upwards failed. The fine new saw less than a month old was jammed; stuck fast. At this stage lassoing the offending branch invariably works but at 25 feet up it was beyond reach of my rope and my skill. The only option was to cut the small understorey beech tree. As the small tree began to fall, the offending branch lost its support, recovered its weight and resumed its gentle bend downwards, releasing its iron-like grip on the saw as it did so.

Such problems would not occur if pruning is done by climbing a ladder and using a handsaw, but in forest conditions this is slow and dangerous. Not only does the uneven ground and equally uneven trunk surface make safe positioning of a ladder difficult, but the sawn off branch itself can hit the ladder and dislodge both it and the one supported! Such skilled operations are best left to tree surgeons and the special theatre of the garden, park or street tree.

Until 1998 all pruning in the wood was with an old style pruning saw consisting of three four-foot long aluminium poles that screwed together. A curved saw blade, welded to an aluminium ring, screwed into the topmost pole length. It was quite heavy, the fine pitch of the screw threads required many turns to tighten the joints home, and so adjusting its length was cumbersome. Also its reach was only about 18 feet. I was persuaded to buy a new high pruner at the biannual fair of Britain's forest and timber industry organised by the Association of Professional Foresters, and known as the 'APF demo'. I was at the event on behalf of the Timber Growers Association to talk about the joys of owning and caring for one's own wood. At one of the many stands situated along a trail on the Yorkshire estate where the event was hosted, I came across Major David Davenport. David grows high quality poplars, along with other woodland crops, on his Herefordshire estate and for a long time has been an enthusiastic pruner. In recent years he has held the franchise of the Silky high pruning saws and related kit. He advertises widely in the trade press, but not until I visited his stand had I even held one of these saws or been subjected to his persuasiveness. An impressive trial cutting and a tempting discount sealed the purchase. I have not regretted it for one minute. The Silky high pruner is as much an improvement over my old saw as the Pentium driven Toshiba laptop on which this book is written is over my first word processor, Alan Sugar's famous 1980s Amstrad 4256. It did a first rate computing job at the time but has long been superseded, the same with the pruner.

But the new pruner had one problem not possessed by its predecessor. On a damp day not long after it was bought, pruning work was finished early as accumulated wettings from little showers of drips began to seep through. After cursorily drying the aluminium lengths they were nested back inside each other and clipped securely into place. Each length fits snugly inside the one below and retracts to about half an inch of its top. It's neatly telescopic and works well provided each length slides smoothly. A week later when next using the pruner, no amount of pulling and tugging would extend and draw out any of the lengths: they were held fast, none of them could be coaxed to move. The red plastic clasps were properly released and the stud clips fully depressed, but there was no movement. The nested lengths of pruning saw appeared glued together. Using a pair of pliers to get a better grip and apply more force only scoured and deformed the soft aluminium with its steel jaws. Penetrating oil was trickled between the nested lengths: the black oil disappeared, but the lengths didn't begin to slide apart and reappear. The magnificent high pruner, capable of extending almost four times its nested length, was incapable of extending at all. What else could be tried? The answer was one of those leaps of thought coined by Edward de Bono in the 1970s as 'lateral thinking'—instead of trying to tug apart the lengths of the fast stuck pruner, use the precious half inch proud lip and tap down each of the lengths to nest them even more snugly. It worked immediately; the sharp tap moved each length a millimetre or two and broke the weak bonds of aluminium hydroxide that residual drops of moisture had caused and which were doubtless the 'glue' sticking the lengths together. As each one was finally drawn out they were indeed still damp and now oily: they were rubbed down thoroughly. I have not been caught out again, the poles are well dried before being nested.

As well as selected beech trees in the main stand, every track-side tree was also high pruned to keep it open to allow Railtrack's vehicles easy passage. This access pruning was not begun until late January, which explains what happened next. One of the track-side trees was a silver birch and the moment the thin, horizontal, stick-like branch was sawn off the freshly exposed wound began weeping sap. A steady drip, almost a trickle, like a tap with a perished washer, continued throughout that morning's work in the wood. A week later the plumber still hadn't repaired the washer and the wound on the birch still dribbled sap! The ground was sodden beneath it. Only in late winter or early spring does root pressure pump sap up the tree as a harbinger of spring, anticipating perhaps the copious quantities of water needed once flushing occurs. But weeping sap for more than a week was surprising. Once before something like it had occurred. A snapped off sycamore twig provided a peg to hang my camera and on fetching it an hour or so later the whole strap, a beautifully woven one Margaret had bought from Tearcraft's catalogue one Christmas, was sopping wet. The tiny branch stub oozed sap and the broad strap wrapping over the broken end had soaked up every drop like a wick.

And so I like pruning, as do many foresters, but rarely is time and money spent doing it. Indeed the debate rages still: does pruning pay? By this is meant, does the better quality knot-free

Pruned Douglas fir tree

wood that one sells 30 or more years after pruning, in the case of conifers, and 80 or more years later for trees like oak and beech, attract a sufficiently better price to make the job worthwhile? For commercial crops it all hinges on the discount rate. Compound interest over 30 years let alone 80 years can be crippling. The argument goes as follows. If it costs the equivalent of £1 per cubic metre of wood to prune selected trees today, in 30 years time how much more must the wood fetch to produce say a moderate 5% return on the investment of doing the pruning? The answer is something like an extra £4 per cubic metre. At even a paltry 5% rate of return, money invested for 30 years quadruples. The figure for 80 years is ninefold! However, the argument falters at two points. Does anyone really think it is possible to make a realistic judgment about timber values in 30 years time let alone over a longer period? Secondly, for the private owner the job of pruning is one that can be done at almost any time, without need for very great skill, and is well suited to casual weekend work. In other words much useful high pruning can be done which needn't be a financial outlay. And it is fine exercise, ideal for a crisp winter's day. These arguments are not robust in the economic sense, but high pruning improves rather than impoverishes a stand of trees (and probably improves the pruner's physique too) and is one of the few operations to add value to one's asset. Enough of economics and indeed of high pruning now that almost a whole chapter has been written. William Pontey wrote an entire book on the subject in 1809, and tree surgeons today have their weighty tomes providing for every detail and consideration of the art. As for those who prune roses sources of advice are legion. However, pruning is not the only woodland job I like.

Pruning may add to the woodland's value economically, taking steps to enhance variety and diversity will add immeasurably to its value for wildlife, which is just as important. Beside practices like leaving dead wood piles and not cutting aging hole-riddled trees which afford nesting sites, three investments in wildlife have been a focus: providing some water by means of a pond—the next but one chapter relates our faltering attempts—developing glades with similarly variable results, and introducing additional wild plants or transplanting some within the wood such as primroses.

Not the birches at Woking, but ones at Petts Wood sketched by my father in the garden where I grew up

The birch tree on Woking Station

The delayed 11.34 from Alton to Waterloo waited at Woking, nearly 20 minutes late. I was going to the biannual meeting of trustees of the Rebecca Hussey charity, a charity set up nearly 200 years ago for the welfare of disadvantaged Africans and 'paying due regard to the furtherance of the Christian religion'. The train was delayed a few minutes more, adding nothing to the enjoyment of a cool damp late October morning with gales forecast. The train waited still at platform 1. Idly looking out of the window across to platform 2, above me, not 10 yards away, was a young birch tree colourlessly etched against the leaden sky. It was nearly leafless but it wasn't a seedling that had struggled up that year. It was two or three years old and as many feet in height. And it was perched on, or rather rooted into the gutter of platform 2's roof. The train finally departed but the recollection of the birch didn't.

How had a tree survived two or three years in such an unlikely place? Not, how was it overlooked for so long by Railtrack or by staff at Woking station, but how could a tree derive enough nourishment and moisture to grow there? On the train and thinking of this chapter about the run of good growing years 1998, 1999 and 2000 the little birch tree's resilience encapsulated it all. The seasons were all good because there was a lot of rain: real British summers good for ducks and trees, and evidently for birches to grow on Woking station's roof.

Even in Britain, blessed with plentiful rain in most years—and 2001 continued the run of wet years—availability of moisture is still what usually determines whether trees grow well and remain clad in deep green leaf through to the first autumn frost. And the last years of the old Millennium were like this—the new millennium really began on 1 January 2001—and they have left an indelible mark on the trees in our wood, a mark which will doubtless long outlast the defiant birch at Woking.

Critical for good growth is rain that falls in spring and summer. Wet weather that keeps soil moisture levels at or near what soil scientists call 'field capacity' allows plants, including trees, to continue to transpire moisture through their leaves uninterrupted. It's like having enough water in the flower vase. Moisture evaporates through tiny holes in leaves, called stomata, that are mostly on the underside of a leaf and are the same holes through which carbon dioxide enters. Carbon dioxide is the fuel for photosynthesis and the building block of plant growth, making wood and other plant parts—nearly half the weight of a tree is carbon—but it can only get in when stomata are open. Close the stomata, which happens in a drought, and photosynthesis slows or stops as carbon dioxide becomes unavailable. Even on warm, dry summer days stomata are closed for much of the time owing to temporary water shortage, but this down time for wood manufacture is shortened if soils are moist and readily able to meet demands. This can't be pushed too far, since very wet soggy soils slow down tree growth because not enough oxygen gets to the roots and they can't breathe—can't respire in physiological terms—and the roots cannot do their work. Nevertheless, in lowland England the main limitation for tree growth is too little rain and soils that become too dry during the summer.

Records from my former research station, the Forestry Commission's research centre at Alice Holt Lodge to the southwest of Farnham on the Surrey/Hampshire border, show how wet the years 1998–2001 were. Alice Holt, as the place is endearingly called (and sometimes misunderstood as people write to 'Dear Alice' or 'Dear Miss Holt') is one of Britain's network of meteorological recording stations. It has a fine reputation for the quality of data kept thanks to the untiring and careful attention of Lorelie

Haydon who more than once has received certificates of excellence from the Meteorological Office. Her daily rainfall registrations reveal the following.

The summer months of these recent years were all at or well above the long-term average for rainfall, a marked contrast to the dry summers of the early to mid 1990s. And the good moist summers followed wet autumns and winters that fully recharged the soils. Her data record too the wet autumn of 2000 which led to so much appalling flooding. In just four months the rainfall registration reached 540 mm compared with the average for September–December at Alice Holt of about 305 mm.

Corroboration of such records, as if it was needed, came from a friend at church, Veronica Pinchen, whose own meticulous registrations in imperial measure for Alton near where we live totalled a record breaking 51.72 ins in year 2000, or getting on for double the town's average of 31 in. More importantly, and despite the extreme wetness of that year's autumn, almost half of Alton's inflated rainfall fell in the months of April–September, just when the trees needed it.

Alice Holt is 21miles from Northdown Plantation as the crow flies, so while not perhaps the nearest meteorological station to the wood it will be representative of central southern England. In the wood itself there is no rain gauge, the arduous task of daily readings at 9 am (10 am in summer) would be impossible, but there is a maximum:minimum thermometer to record temperature extremes. The best that can be done is to inspect the pond to see how wet things have been in the preceding weeks! The feel of the wood too can also help: how dry it is under foot, how luxuriant weed growth is, whether the dog's mercury is wilting on not, and even whether there is a puddle in the ruts of the track at the bottom of the wood. For the trees themselves it is quite another matter. They are highly unlikely to wilt with their deepest roots drawing on moisture from the chalky subsoil and chalk rubble parent material beneath. Nevertheless, with most roots in the topsoil, whether it's damp or dry will make a big difference to whether the stomata in leaves and needles stay open or closed. A wet summer is good for tree growth, much new wood is manufactured and the tree records this not daily, like Lorelie's rainfall registrations, but annually by the width of the ring of new wood laid down that year. A wide ring shows a good year for growth.

Another indication of how wet recent years have been was

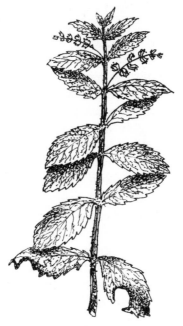

Dog's mercury

provided by our neighbour, Mike. He draws water from a bore-hole that taps the massive chalk aquifer beneath both our lands and the Hampshire Downs as a whole. The drilling engineers told him that normally they would reach the water table in our area at a depth of 40 m, but when Mike's hole was bored in 1995, after the dry years of the early 1990s, 46 m was required. Today the water table is back to its usual level and rising as wet years have replenished the aquifer.

Good growing years are also recorded by trees in other ways. For many conifers the length of the internode, which is the distance between whorls of branches up the stem, is a good measure since in temperate climates one internode is added each year. It doesn't work in the tropics where many internodes or growth spurts can occur in a season. And in temperate countries it is not quite as simple as the width of the current annual ring since the length of the internode is mainly influenced by the previous year's weather when the bud for the coming year was laid down. Good conditions give it the potential to elongate well, poor conditions and it won't. Apart from a couple of scraggy Corsican pines left behind when the pines were felled in 1992, the only conifers in the wood are about 60 well-grown Douglas firs. When they are felled in a few years time both their annual rings and internode lengths ought to reveal whether 1998–2001 was really that good.

Beech trees have another device that records each year's growth. On the twigs there are narrow bands of fine wrinkles or creases in the delicate bark marked off at intervals along the twig as it thickens into a branch. These delineate where each year's shoot extension starts and can be traced down a branch sometimes back 15 or 20 years. In good years shoots extend well, in poor years less well, so the distance between bands of wrinkles records, like the graduations on a rain gauge, how good growing conditions were.

In November 2001 two large trees were felled in the wood, a mishappen 45-year-old beech and a dangerously leaning ash. The ash was cut as wood for turning for David Foot, the chairman of Hampshire woodturners association. The timber was decayed at the base, stained in some of the heartwood, but the tree was an unexpected 130 years old; its height and diameter had suggested only 70 or 80 years. The most recent annual rings were too irregular to confirm good growth. On the upside of the leaning trunk they were very broad as if the tree had been laying down hawsers of wood fibres to keep it guyed, while on the underside the rings were barely discernible. All trees react to stress such as a lean, a bend, and the special strain branches have, and put on wood differentially to compensate. Conifers tend to buttress by building compression wood, while broadleaves, like the leaning ash, do the opposite and add cabling called tension wood. In both cases the one-sided growth causes the central pith of the tree to be far from the actual middle of the cross-section which can also become

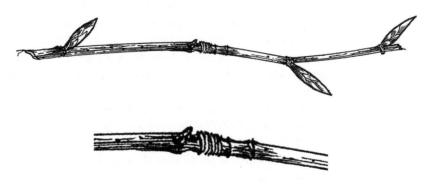

Beech twig with bark creases

eccentric in shape. The ash did show that growth in the last two decades was far better than it had been in its early life. The younger beech had certainly grown vigorously in the late 1990s and the twigs from high up in the crown showed long distances between the tight crinkles, sometimes 50 cm or more. The trees in the wood seem to be growing well.

Good growth of trees is not confined to Northdown plantation. The Forestry Commission's annual surveys of tree health, maintained since the mid-1980s, show that many of our forest trees like oak and beech are thicker in foliage, and it is therefore presumed healthier, than they were in the late 1980s or early 1990s. Undoubtedly the run of wet years has been beneficial. And to this good news can be added a report by the European Forest Institute, based in Joenssu in Finland, who carried out a detailed survey of 10 countries across Europe. In 1997 they reported that in every country, with the exception of just two sites, trees were growing better now than they were 100 years ago. Of course, this is not mainly or even marginally due to more rainfall, but it is a fact worth noting amid all the environmental gloom. The reasons suggested by the Institute do, however, relate to pollution.

Increasing amounts of several gases in the air we breathe, notably carbon dioxide, which is largely responsible for the greenhouse effect, and various oxides of nitrogen are thought to have a 'fertilizer effect'. These gases are added as we burn fossil fuels like oil, gas and coal, and destroy rain forests and drive our cars. However, a higher concentration of carbon dioxide aids photosynthesis and the oxides of nitrogen dissolve in rain so watering the earth with measurable amounts of extra 'free' fertilizer as nitrates and nitrites. These effects are happening more than ever and so, very reasonably, the argument goes that such inputs, although caused by pollution, are making trees grow more vigorously.

The observed improvement in tree growth is also thought to arise from cessation of some harmful practices as well. The one most commonly suggested is that we no longer gather or rake up masses of branches, twigs and leaves, what is called forest litter, for fuel or for bedding for livestock which was stock-in-trade use of the woodland floor up to about 100 years ago. Such practices undoubtedly looted the woodland of huge amounts of organic matter and plant nutrients and the soil was impoverished. Not surprisingly tree growth under such conditions was not as productive as it might be. This litter raking is still practised in China and is believed to be why successive crops of their much planted Chinese fir show declining yields, a problem rarely found elsewhere.

Better growth is not confined to the trees. Also doing well in wet years are mushrooms and fungi in early autumn, and the luxuriance of weed growth especially in the rides. The arrival of plants such as lady's smock, also called cuckoo plant, spotted for the first time in 1996 by my mother, may also reflect greater dampness. But the same wet weather may be causing monocultures of nettles to spread ever more vigorously, coarse grasses to increase, and bramble patches to explode. Delectable flowers lose out. Changing browsing patterns and increased numbers of rabbits and deer are an equally likely explanation, so it is intemperate to blame the otherwise welcome rain.

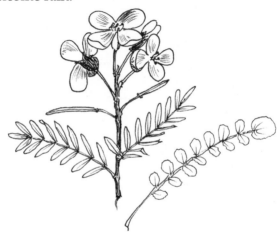

Lady's smock

I was back at Woking two days later, again because of cancelled and delayed trains in the sorry autumn of 2000 for Britain's beleaguered and ill-managed railways. With ample time to kill, I crossed to Platform 1 to look again at the birch tree. Up and down the roof gutter there were three, and a couple of the now ubiquitous buddleia which have been sprinkled so liberally as butterfly fodder around stations and railway yards. After this arboricultural detour and still waiting for the delayed 16.46 for Alton, I looked back to Platform 1. It, too, proudly sported a fine pair of birch trees in the gutter. The last few years really must have been good growing seasons. A year later Railtrack eventually removed the trees, and presumably one day will eventually get round to modernizing the rail network too.

Fungi proliferate in wet years

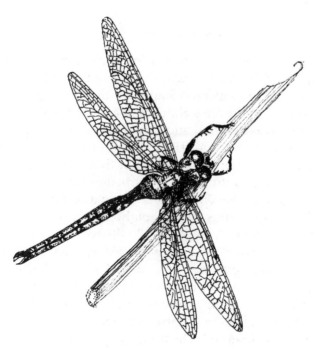

12

The pond problem

For some time we had thought about constructing a pond. The wood has no running water, no stream or spring, and no still water beyond the puddles that form for two or three days after very heavy rain in the ruts along a stretch of the track that runs beside the railway line. Two events in late 1995 prompted action: on 11th October the water tank departed (with our blessing) and on the 14th a mechanical digger, a JCB, arrived to open a trench to bury an electric cable along the bottom track, with or without its puddles, to Railtrack's electrical substation. The loss of the tank meant no water at all in the wood, while the arrival of the digger afforded possible muscle for excavation. Hastily on that October day, during a warm autumnal spell with temperatures of 20°C or more, a small, butterfly shaped pond was marked out in the rough open ground that continues the cross-ride into what is now Tanglewood. Really it was two ponds joined by a narrow channel. But six days later, by the 20th October, the digger was gone and the pond undug.

For the rest of the winter the sticks delineating the pond's outline remained in place like a child's dot-to-dot puzzle. The puzzle for me was how, or rather who, was going to do the digging? Hiring a JCB just to excavate a few bucketfuls of soil seemed an unnecessary expense. Some desultory researching of pond construction and enquiries about council grants kept the idea alive, but attention was diverted and focused on our first open day scheduled for 6th May. Several friends from our church came to that open day and brought the suggestion that the youth group could dig the pond in return for a barbeque and campfire: it sounded a fair exchange. Seven weeks later, on a languid Saturday in June, digging began, muscled by eight young people, three adults and two children. A depth of 30–40 cm was excavated, much chalk rubble revealed, and many blisters earned. Earned too was a supper of jacket potatoes and melted cheese, lashings of coleslaw, unlimited crisps, and the special relish of toasting marsh mallows on sticks to a crisping without and gooing within. June had been dry, the work had been hard and this unhealth-conscious meal was thoroughly deserved. The pond was no longer an outline and excavation no longer a puzzle, it had begun to take shape.

Further digging during July and early August with the help of one, two and sometimes all three sons along with a friend, Andrew Susans, completed the excavation. By mid August all was ready for the critical second stage of lining the pond. The pond's bottom and sides were bright white but porous as a sieve. Every square inch of the freshly exposed chalk rubble would need covering and making watertight. Traditional puddling with clay was ruled out since none was nearby and, in my usual cost-cutting approach, just a single thickness of heavy-duty (125 micron) black polythene, as used on farms for baling silage, would be risked. My team of three sons and Andrew assembled in the wood on 21st August to line the pond.

We allocated a whole day for the job with just a lunch break. It was difficult to know whether one day would be enough time and the notes reveal anxiety and irritation at slow service over lunch at the Little Chef at Popham as valuable minutes slipped by. I even complained, but this was unreasonable since we were in the holiday month of August. Nevertheless we, or at least I, was anxious to get on.

First we finished building the banks, particularly on the lower side of the gentle slope, relying totally on guesswork to judge the levels. Then we scoured every inch of the pond for sharp flints, stones, and twigs that might pierce the plastic lining. Using a small sledgehammer Stephen proved adept at flattening protrusions and Jon swept the floor of the pond to tidy it far better than he had ever tidied his bedroom as a teenager. Ben and Andrew cut back grasses and shrubs around the edge. All was spic and span and ready for the next step, gleaned from researches into pond construction. Secondly, therefore, before laying the lining, the smooth surfaces of the bottom and sides were covered with newspapers, several pages thick, which had been accumulated in the garage in the preceding weeks. All of Britain's broadsheets were represented as well as the odd *Daily Mail* and also many pages of the thick, blotting paper like sheets from surplus books of Braille. As these layers were put in place water was sprinkled to hold them down. All was now ready for the most delicate stage.

Along the cross ride the 11 x 8 metre roll of black silage plastic was carefully unwound and cut in two. One piece was 6 x 8 metres and the other 5 x 8 metres to fit the slightly different sizes of the two parts of the pond, the butterfly's two wings. Ben and I carried these linings and gently draped them over the papered ponds allowing their weight to settle them in place. The others helped spread out the lining, liberally leaving plenty of folds and 'spare' plastic so that it would become seated into every corner and every

recess without stretching. Then, taking off my trainers and gingerly stepping onto the shiny black skin of plastic, the lining was tucked loosely home. The many layers of newspaper did their work. No hole could be seen and no bump or sharpness felt through stockinged feet: no protrusion pierced the plastic film. Or so we hoped. Carefully sieved soil was spread over the bottom and along the banks to pin down the sides, and then further soil was added to build the banks higher and tamped into place holding the lining beneath. Thus was the pond lined, very, very carefully, but not perfectly. I had overlooked that where the banks were steepest the plastic film was still exposed: soil covered the bottom, the lower 'slopes' and the top of the lining, but in between the taught plastic was unprotected. Only when the pond was full of water would all be covered.

Before leaving we posted a warning sign of 'No Entry' and fastened a ribbon of white polythene all around the pond to deter intruders, including we hoped any deer—if unable to read, at least wary of something new! We tidied up the site, cleaned the spades and stowed everything into the car and left to wait on the Lord to send rain. He did. He blessed us with over an inch over Thursday night and Friday.

On Saturday Ben and I went to the wood to check on the pond. Muddy water formed pools a couple of inches deep. The delicate sides seemed intact but taught, stretched by the weight of water, and the tops of the banks were a little exposed. As we were sowing grass and wildflower seed on the bare earth we suddenly saw them and they saw us, the three police heading up the path from the direction of the Railtrack's substation. As related in chapter 1, the same investigations a week or two later peppered the carefully constructed pond banks with metal tipped probes. Nothing was found as there was no evidence of exploratory digging, but whether the delicate plastic lining was still intact remained unknown. When Margaret and Stephen came a week later to inspect our efforts the pond still looked sound, a mole had burrowed into the soft earth of the bank, and the water depth was now about five inches since more heavy rain had fallen that week. We left satisfied, but anxious still about the unprotected lining.

What I should have done was fill the pond on the day the lining was laid. Although this wouldn't stop animals burrowing from underneath, nor the utterly unforeseen probings by police, it would have prevented tiny claws, larger paws and cloven hooves from testing the shiny surface to reach the slowly enlarging pools. Piping could have been run about 350 m from Mike's newly dug borehole and the idea had been raised with him in early September. It was also important to warn his children about the dangers of the pond, and indeed this was one reason why it was located at the far side of the wood away from his smallholding. In the end neither piping water nor ferrying quantities in 44 gallon drums (the other idea) was resorted to, and we simply left the matter of the filling to the falling of rain. Already wildlife was beginning to find this oasis. We surprised a pair of wood pigeons slaking their thirst and tiny footprints suggested other interested visitors unable to read the 'No Entry' sign.

By the autumn equinox, 21st September, concerns seemed justified, the water level had definitely gone down. Or was it that September was dry with only an inch of rain? I began bringing water in 4½ gallon containers on every visit because in early October we were holding a second open day and were to receive a Centre of Excellence Award from the Forestry Commission. The pond needed to look like one and not just a muddy hole. But such amounts of water were paltry. On one occasion another receptacle was added to transport water, but only as far as the car park outside my mother's flat, by which time it had slurped, filled the car's floor behind the driver's seat and soaked the grey carpet to leave that cloying smell of damp every car owner knows. By late October the bigger pond was still filling but the water level in the smaller one was, at best, static. The lining seemed intact though the notes that day record: 'Am I impatient or is it leaking slowly or what?' Further woodland diary entries take up the story.

Wind and rain were forecast for the last week of October, but owing to work in Kenya a month passed before another visit to the wood. By the 27th November and despite the month being wet, the smaller upper, pond was shallow and obviously leaking. The lower one was a little deeper. The next visit, after Christmas, found both ponds frozen with precious little in the top one. Some relining was now inevitable. For the next two months the notes fall silent: the records tell of thinning in Nain's Copse, of early signs of spring, of cutting firewood and of other woodland happenings, but the pond is forgotten. On 1st March the record baldy declares: 'February wet, ponds not filling'.

The next pond entry is 20th May and the remark, 'pond has some water!' Despite a wet June nothing further is said, and even despite a wet autumn the next pond-related entry is not until Boxing Day which states 'Despite much rain, pond empty'. This was how 1997 ended. As for 1998, the pond receives no mention: I was defeated by ignorance, by impatience and perhaps by police investigation.

We didn't give up, and more than a year later and succoured by the support of the Everett family and friends a late January day in early 1999 found us relining the bigger pond. Dr Chris Everett, from the village of Holybourne where we live, and his brother and a friend from Monmouth unpeeled the faulty lining. It was surprisingly hard to lift and surprisingly dry beneath. A few ragged holes suggested gnawing by rats or possibly tearing by deer slots had penetrated the plastic and so pulled the plug of the original pond. The newspaper underlay was mostly intact and we added further layers of *Independents, Daily Telegraphs, Evening Standards* and *Alton Heralds*. Then for the new lining. Spending hundreds of pounds on a proprietary butyl liner still seemed exorbitant and so we stayed with silage plastic, but this time lavished a whole roll on the lower pond folding it like a sandwich with further layers of paper as the meat in the middle. We also papered over the exposed surface and on top of all this laid an offcut of plastic. It was like a MacDonalds' triple decker.

This second attempt at construction was in winter, rather than high summer as previously. Not only is it a wetter time of year, there is also less evaporation and we hoped less demand for drinking water by the woodland's inhabitants. Regrettably, our renewed efforts were at the end of one of the wettest years on record, but it didn't matter. Rain fell in the days that followed and my notes return to recording water levels and aquatic activity on almost every visit. In late February two successive visits note 'Pond slowly filling'. The same comment with the adjective 'still' is added in late March, after which regular comment disappears, this time content that all is going well and not from loss of interest. Indeed, by late April, there is rejoicing: 'Pond fuller than it ever has been and close to maximum depth'. But this revealed another shortcoming. During construction, levelling judged by eye had not even been close: the now full pond with its perfect, gravity levelled surface showed the lining on the upper side finished six inches above the lower side. This exposed a narrow zone of black lining to wind, wear and wildlife, but at least there were now two layers.

On 1st May a tiny water-skater appeared, the pond's first truly aquatic inhabitant. In June heavy rain kept the pond full and the wood was lush with growth; stinging nettles were head high. Indeed, the damp of recent months even persuaded local councils and water authorities to declare for the first time in years that there would be no hosepipe bans for watering gardens that summer. In July the notes declare the pond to be full, although the month was very dry and hot. Indeed, I exulted over a pond at the crossroads half-a-mile from Dummer village, which is passed on the way to the wood, that was waterless—it clearly leaks, filling and emptying in concert with rain—and ours was full!

In August, my mother visited the pond. We were on the way back from Wantage in Berkshire and stopped for half-an-hour. July's drought had wilted the dog's mercury, it lay exhausted, roots no longer reaching sufficient moisture from the thin topsoil. We reached the pond and disturbed a female blackbird sipping anxiously. All was still and warm. A dragonfly hovered, turquoise green and purple tipped, darted, criss-crossing about a foot above the calm unruffled surface. Water skaters slid back and forth, erratic in time and space, but doubtless full of intent in their two dimensional world. A week later friends from church, the Bavage family who had been so helpful with history of the railway, spotted damsel flies and the brilliant colours of the dragonfly. Steven Bavage spied leeches in the smaller, almost empty, pond that still awaits re-lining, adding these to his inventory of crickets and grasshoppers. A fortnight later heavy rain ensured the pond was brim full; it had finally come of age.

Pond entries tailed off and are confined to occasional remarks about more deer slots—it is becoming their water-hole—and further sightings of the turquoise and purple-tipped dragon fly. Both before and after a long overseas trip to southern Africa in the autumn, terse comment merely notes 'pond full'. Entries for year 2000 are few, a case of no news is good news. In May woodpigeon feathers lay scattered near the pond like confetti marking where a fox or a sparrow hawk caught its prey. August saw a pair of starlings fight over drinking rights with much screeching and general noisiness, and red campion, the first in the wood, are flowering on the pond's northern bank, presumably coming from the wild seed sown three years before. Later in the month pond weed, elodea, is added: such confidence at last! All remaining entries simply state 'pond full', which was hardly surprising with the wettest ever

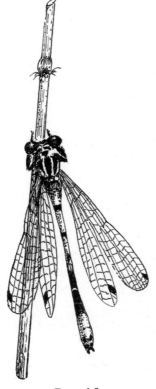

Damsel fly

autumn, until the final entry of the year which notes it is frozen following overnight snow just after Christmas.

The woodland diary has recorded the rise, fall, and then rise again of attempts at pond building and impounding a little water to diversify the woodland. There is still the smaller pond to re-line. And we must decide what to do with sticks and leaves that accumulate in the pond each autumn, and whatever else arrives at other times as youngsters find it irresistible. Folds of the temporary lining still 'float' near the surface and occasionally a *Daily Telegraph* surfaces, soggy and pulpy from water-logging rather than reactionary politics. The pond is now part of the wood, and God has filled it.

The pond brought water back to the wood. The grey tank ended up with Melvyn via an exchange with our neighbour Mike who each year swipes the rides in return. A good tank has found a good home. The age of the trees and the kind they are, mainly broadleaves, and the passing of the age of steam and attendant sparks from engine funnels, makes fire risk minimal and an accessible and substantial water supply not needed. The age of conservation is with us and the new pond is a small contribution with its water for wildlife to drink, to skate upon, to hover over and perhaps one day to swim in.

13

Coping with overgrown sycamore coppice

Although many visits to the wood are on my own, company is always a pleasure. It is positively desirable when working with a chainsaw, if only as a safety precaution since chainsaw accidents are common, invariably gory and mostly happen far from anyone to find you by chance. Having a mobile phone is a must, but company is better.

For many people the idea of working in a woodland appeals, and not only as an escape from gardening for the half of humanity who find it a chore. For some it is rustic and 'back to nature', for others it is developing skills no longer commonplace like coppicing; or the satisfaction can come from helping with woodland work so that trees in decades to come will be the best they can be. For others, it is creating better habitat for wildlife, or simply that cutting and collecting firewood on a crisp, invigorating day in late autumn or winter with the low sun shafting through the trees, is reason enough. For all, though, there is the sense of getting away, the sense of peace and solitude far from office, internet, and emails or from shops, shifts, and superstores. There are other reasons too, but whatever they are, offers of help and company are readily accepted.

Regular help has mostly been directed to thinning the lanky drawn-up sycamore coppice in Nain's Copse for firewood, high pruning of beech and Douglas fir trees in the main block, some coppicing of old hazel, and what is called 'cleaning' the young trees in Taid's Wood—the cutting out of unwanted growth, singling stems and pruning off low branches. Also in the category of 'regular' is swiping of rides that Mike Fisher does once or twice a year to keep nettles and grass to manageable proportions. Occasional and very welcome help created the pond and then 2½ years later completed its relining after the original had failed. And, after most open days, someone has kindly gathered up the notices or collected the trail direction arrows and other markers as their help with tidying up. Occasionally, unsuspecting car passengers on journeys that pass near the wood are the company. In summer this usually means taking them on a 15-minute rush around the wood to visit the eight grey squirrel hoppers to replenish bait supply or to make sure it is not clogged, while at other times it's more a check that all is well and nothing's amiss, and rubbish is not cluttering the entrance. Of course they can stay in the car, though more often than not the lure of fresh air, the countryside or simply curiosity is enough. We climb the gate and set off for the hasty tour of inspection. I enjoy all these ways of sharing what is fun to me, and with what, as Margaret pointed out, is my hobby.

It was many years before I realized that the wood was 'my hobby'. It was a liberating thought, though I hope free of any unprofessional connotation of a 'hobby farmer'. But hobby it is, in the time I spend there, from the pleasure I derive, and the enthusiasm I have of wanting to share it with others.

On one occasion our church's former minister, The Revd Kenneth McIntosh, came over to Northdown Plantation. The morning's work was high pruning and together, laden with poles, saws, gloves and hard hats, we walked down the main track and then set off to the right at a tangent just below the cross-rides to negotiate the uneven ground, the debris of fallen branches and other knee-high obstacles to one of the patches of Douglas firs. The sleek Japanese high pruner that has proved such a boon in recent years had yet to be bought, and our main tools were the old 5-foot long aluminium poles that screwed together just like a chimney sweep's rods, but without the flexibility. A curved saw, reminiscent of a scimitar, screws into the end. I had two of the curved saws and three 5-foot lengths. We shared these out. Ken, who is taller than me, pruned the lower branches with one length of pole and saw and I used two lengths of pole to reach the higher, more tricky ones. We also shared out the two orange hard hats: falling branches, even small ones, can hurt.

Ken's wife, Anne, had thoughtfully suggested the idea of her husband coming to the wood. The welcome help led not only to physical pruning, but some spiritual branching out over coffee as we talked about our Christian faith. Douglas firs are easy trees to prune. Their branches, though sometimes numerous, are thin and two or three sharp downward strokes of the saw usually severs them. I briefly showed Ken how to cut them off flush without scarring the bark and then we set to work a few yards apart on the 30 or so trees in the clump. Resting after about half-an-hour, I saw Ken intently pruning an indifferent oak just outside the clump of firs, and shouted out not to bother. It then occurred to me that while explaining the niceties of pruning forest trees, exactly which trees were to receive our attentions had not been discussed. Although firs and oaks seem as different as chalk from cheese, why should they appear very obviously so to anyone else? In woodlands, trees are trees with trunks and branches, just as in a flock, sheep are sheep with woolly coats that I can't tell apart, but the shepherd readily can—and I hadn't said which trees to prune.

The largest group of helpers, apart from our church's young people who excavated the pond, has been the doctor and his family. They helped reline the pond, but their first visit was to Nain's Copse. Chris Everett, for many years an Alton GP and authority on pregnancy calculation (indeed he invented the simple but effective 'obdisk' to help predict the happy event) came with his son Sean and his cousins Ben and John Daniel. I mention this because not only had the Daniels journeyed all the way from east Wales, but Ben is a skilled chainsaw operative. Their visit in January 1998 occurred when thinning through the four acres of Nain's Copse was becoming a struggle. The aim was to favour the best stems of ash and sycamore to grow with the scattered oak standards as an uneven-aged mixed woodland. The thinning work had begun a year earlier mainly with assistance from Ben, my youngest son, and sometimes his friends Andrew and Will. It proved a big job to tackle and progress was slow. Help from the doctor's party was a sinecure and many tall slender stems of overgrown coppice were cut to leave the best one or two on each stump. The felled trees were cut into 4-foot lengths, and those unskilled at chainsaw work manhandled the logs into piles for firewood.

This help was both stimulating and salutary. Ben Daniel, as a trained and fully qualified chainsaw operator, and an instructor in the skill at Usk college, showed up my amateurish technique albeit acquired from long experience. Although mercifully without an

accident in more than 30 years, compared with Ben I was poorly equipped, poorly skilled in chain sharpening, and perhaps too adventurous in felling dangerously hung-up trees. His help was a stimulus, and several lessons learned that morning purged some of my more risky practices.

The thinning in Nain's Copse was a silvicultural challenge. I sometimes ask myself whether it is even the best way to handle the highly unusual mixture of scattered oak standards with very over-grown sycamore and ash coppice. The original high stocking of oak was reduced in 1994, but developing the ash and sycamore has been problematic. The aim is to create mixed woodland by allow-ing the best coppice stems, many already poking into the upper canopy, to develop their crowns and become fully part of the stand, a process called 'storing' coppice. Eventually it should look like high forest, a delightful broadleaved woodland of three or four different species and a wide range of ages. But will it? And, if so, then what happens?

By 2001 about half of the dense, tight, drawn up coppice of Nain's Copse had been thinned. The parts first treated look all right, though even after five years the thinned sycamore show few signs of responding. Forty-year-old stems of sycamore, 70 or 80 feet high and jostling the oak canopy, have narrow, conical crowns little different from the way young trees of this species look when perhaps five years old. Although with more growing space, the growing tips of shoots and twigs appear slow to branch out, liter-ally, and slow to ramify and occupy the room available; their leaves are like a tuft atop a long stem, shaped more like a child's toy Christmas tree than a lollipop. The few thinned ash coppice look more normal. These observations of thinning response were supplemented by measurement—a forest scientist is ever curious to know the consequences of actions—and the stem diameters of about 20 sycamore and 20 ash, all left as stored coppice after thin-ning, were measured. Four years later they were re-measured. The sycamore had barely grown, two or three millimetres a year at most had been added to the diameter. By contrast the normally slender ash had thickened twice as fast. What the long-term result will be remains unsure, but the experience so far supports the forester's adage of 'a little and often' to handle the change gently. The late Lord Bolton would take this conclusion to task since his *Profitable Forestry*, written in the 1950s, strongly advocated heavy thinning to sort out neglected crops like Nain's Copse. He described the common risks of wind throw and uprooting as exaggerated. He had, or rather his Yorkshire estates have, some of Britain's finest sycamore stands. I mention his book specifically, not only for its relevance, but because it was kindly sent to me by a reader who had enjoyed *A Wood of Our Own*. He didn't suggest there were any lessons to be learnt, but reading about Lord Bolton's experience was valuable.

Because progress in Nain's Copse has been slow, in the last two years an alternative way of thinning the remaining area has followed a 'make-safe' policy. The best stems were searched out—those that were straight, with reasonable crowns and without obvious defects—and marked by tying a ribbon of plastic. Ash was always given preference over sycamore. Each selected tree was then visited and any nearby tree competing severely was felled. This would ensure that the ones awarded a ribbon would at least not suffer if a few more years' neglect ensued. At this stage the best plan is probably to include thinning of Nain's Copse at the same time that the beech of Northdown Plantation is next thinned in 2003 or 2004. The trees cut out in the 'make-safe' thinning have been left where they fell, being too few to be worth using, a practice labelled appropriately as 'thinning to waste'. The thinning simply ensures that the trees one wants to keep for a long time are not prejudiced by inferior, perhaps more vigorous competitors. It's not a spacing out like thinning among newly germinated seedlings, but more resembles a dead-heading of roses or pansies to encourage the best adjacent blooms. Hopefully it has secured the best trees in Nain's Copse for the future.

Since acquiring Nain's Copse in 1994, and as a result of the gradual thinning out winter after winter, it has become the principal source of firewood. A sawing horse was erected near the great oaks and a chicken wire mesh bin sited nearby for the cut logs. The firewood is, of course, mostly sycamore, which dries quite readily. Occasionally there is some ash which, as everyone knows, is the best firewood since it can be burnt without seasoning, though even ash does better if it is allowed to dry for a month or two.

After moving to the village of Holybourne in Hampshire I advertised home delivery of firewood in 10 kg bags. The response was meagre even though the outrageous prices of bagged firewood charged by garages and garden centres were well undercut. In the end this was not such a bad thing, as so many other commitments claimed our time and because of a singular problem in the firewood cutting, bagging and delivery chain that sapped our efficiency. A small Stihl chainsaw was used to fell the sycamore and ash coppice stems and convert them to four or five foot lengths. These were stacked and at least a year later, when well seasoned, were cut into the 8' or 9' billets suitable for the grate, again using the chainsaw. Bigger logs were split by axe. Logs were then bagged up in bright tomato red polypropylene vegetable sacks that weighed about 10 kg when full. Such bags were easily manhandled both by me into the car and by the customer into their garage or to the hearth. Cutting and splitting work proceeded more or less at the same rate, but bagging of firewood was slow and frustrating. As neatly cut and cleanly split logs were placed into the polypropylene bags their ends would snag on the mesh and would need freeing up or easing into place to be well packed down. Stiffened fingers from winter cold made things worse, while wearing gloves was clumsy. Bag filling became a nuisance to the point that a solution had to be found.

Since I had originally bought 1000 bags in one of those moments of irrational confidence and still had—and still have—several hundred, switching to a less snag prone container was not an option. Thinking what to do became one of those topics mulled over during a boring presentation at a conference or when stuck in a traffic jam. So is borne an obsession. For something like a year the riddle of what to do eddied around the mind. Amongst my many schemes were a plastic chute made from a large ice-cream container, waste paper basket or small kitchen dustbin followed by sleeving the polypropylene sack over the plastic container, like a sheath, so that its smooth, shiny and snag-free sides would let logs pack down easily. Then, I imagined, the plastic lining could be deftly withdrawn to leave a neatly filled bag. However, on two occasions suitably sized containers were even bought and their ends sawn off to try out the system. One proved a shade too large for the bags, the other lost all rigidity once the bottom was cut off and proved unworkable. So urgent had the desire to fabricate a device become, that once in Istanbul to visit friends I cried out for them to stop when we passed a market stall piled high with plastic containers of every conceivable dimension and colour. Twenty rummaging minutes later, the perfect container still eluded. Thus the numerous polypropylene sacks continued to catch and snag the short logs and continued to hold up the smooth running of the tiny firewood business.

The end of my obsession came with a novel thought, which was so simple and obvious that it wasn't lateral thinking more a random thought that, statistically, was bound to surface eventually. Throughout all the early bagging of firewood the short logs were packed down horizontally just as one builds a wood-pile. This, the natural orientation, meant that each split log presented two ends and at least four pointed corners to get snagged. Packing them this way also required opening the polypropylene net bags in a rectangular shape like a letterbox. Simply standing the logs on end as one would stack cans of beer halved the chance of snagging and solved the packing problem. Indeed, split logs packed in this way snugly fitted together like segments of an orange and also shaped the bag more like a sack of potatoes. This single adjustment to orientation so speeded up bagging that the cutting, splitting and packing team kept pace with each other. It's just a pity that the thought of beer cans didn't occur sooner, and a pity that each winter there seems less and less time for cutting firewood. Hundreds of bright tomato red polypropylene bags still languish in our garden shed. But at least I now know how to fill them more easily with logs.

Thinning out clumps of tall slender sycamore has not been the only over-grown coppice to attend to. When Northdown Plantation was bought by the Forestry Commission in the 1950s they set about converting the 'devastated' woodland to an orderly plantation of pine and beech trees. Previously the wood appears to have been a mixture of oaks and sycamore with a hazel understorey. Whether it was a true coppice with standards is difficult to tell, or whether it copied the planting of Nain's Copse is now obscure. What is not obscure is that throughout Northdown Plantation, underneath the beech, are over-mature hazel. The hazel clumps are not everywhere; in places there are several, elsewhere none at all. They are at their thickest where the beech trees are fewest and their dark shade has not suppressed them. Or is this the wrong way round? Are there few beeches where the hazel clumps are because the shrub's vigour suppressed newly planted beech and pine 45 years ago? Or is this wrong too? Did the hazel re-growth initially keep up with the young planted crop until eventually overtopped by it except where the beech was killed 20 or 25 years ago by rabbit or squirrel damage, as the widespread staining and scarring of the annual rings seen on thinning stumps suggests? We may never know, but in most places the understorey

Hazel twigs and catkins

hazel added nothing to the woodland and would interfere with thinning the beech.

Where the hazel had survived, it was an old mix of thick stems and new slender shoots that splayed in all directions. We tackled it at the same time as thinning Nain's Copse. The densest patches were near the Douglas firs that Ken and I pruned. All three sons helped since clearing overmature hazel is particularly tricky chain-saw work, but the day that remains most clearly remembered was when our eldest son Jon and a friend from church, Ian, had come along. Ian, a builder by trade, possesses that enviable ability to turn his hand to almost anything. Their support was invaluable that day.

It was a Saturday in late January and the three of us had set out from Alton when the temperature was subzero. And it was subzero when we arrived. It was still subzero when we stopped for an early coffee. All morning a biting east wind blew unabated, and the normally congenial woodland shorn in mid-winter of its leafy shelter, was no match for this Siberian blast. The light dusting of snow further emphasised the cold and ensured that while ears and other exposed extremities were wind chilled, feet and toes felt frozen. Only vigorous exercise could pump enough blood to keep us warm and we set about the cold-stiffened hazel with gusto. As the clumps fell apart and stems and branches fell to the ground, inevitably intertwined, Jon and Ian cut out and trimmed up pea sticks and bean poles—heralds of warmer times to come. Another herald was the happy company of a pair of robins who hopped around us, searching for some morsel uncovered by the exertions of that winter's day. They found plenty of ladybird beetles hiding in crevices of bark and crotches of twigs.

As clearing proceeded the chainsaw kept stalling and the chain itself kept falling off its guidebar. Cold might have contributed to stalling, but I ran the chain too slack, cold fingers unwilling to unglove, find the screwdriver and tighten the adjusting screw the necessary quarter turn. The guidebar by that time was quite old and worn and along with poor technique probably made things worse. Chainsaws need careful looking after. We abandoned the hazel with all its tricks and travails and turned to cutting firewood logs, where the saw is held vertical and steady. Enough logs were cut to fill six bags before the saw stalled for the last time as it ran out of fuel.

Hearing the activity, and the intermittent screams of the chainsaw, Mike called by to offer us a welcome cup of tea—we had long since consumed Margaret's flask of coffee. In exchange he departed with a bag of firewood and also my agreement to put a small gate in the hedge next to where he had recently lodged his mobile home, to allow ready access to the ride that runs inside the wood adjacent to his smallholding. Mike walks round the wood most days, in winter and in summer, and provides immense help in keeping and eye on things.

That cold winter's day was almost the last for clearing hazel in the main block, though there are still several clumps that need cutting. And there are plenty of hazel in Tanglewood and plenty of every other scrub and shrub species too, but they won't be cleared, for theirs is another story.

Moschatel

Tanglewood

When we bought the 7.5 acres of woodland adjoining Northdown Plantation in 1994, it consisted of two quite different parts. The larger part—the old Ashe pightle—we named Nain's Copse since it is a coppice with standards: the coppice is a few stored ash and numerous sycamore and the standards are oak trees. We named it after my mother: as I think I have explained Nain, pronounced 'nine', is Welsh for grandmother, and is what our boys call her as a delightful distinction from their granny, my mother-in-law. However, the smaller part of what we bought, about three acres, has no ashes and no sycamores, either as trees or coppice, and only a few scraggy oaks in one corner. Indeed, there is very little in it of timber value and parts are almost impenetrable owing to the tangle of growth and so we have given it the name, informally at least, of Tanglewood.

My wife, Margaret, had seen a cottage called Tanglewood in the Devonshire village of Doddiscombsleigh near Exeter where from time to time we stay at the Nobody Inn. She felt this name perfectly described this rarely visited and least managed corner of the wood. There's even a hint of Tanglewood tales, Nathaniel

Hawthorne's 19th century children's Greek mythology, with Medusa-like creepers and as impenetrable as any Minotaur's maze. How Tanglewood came to be like it is, one can only speculate. As a spear-shaped triangle of land it is delineated on the 1911 OS maps, but unlike the nearly square block of Nain's Copse to its east and the newly planted Northdown Plantation to its south, no tree symbols were marked on it. Clearly it wasn't woodland; it appears a blank 'field'. Why this small triangular field was not planted is a mystery, because evidently it was not retained for agricultural use either. What we do know is that its northern edge is the boundary between the old Litchfield Grange Estate and the vast acres the Portal family owned: the tithe map shows this demarcation very clearly. When Northdown was planted a straight edge, perhaps to economise on fencing, was followed leaving high and dry without access and apparently without purpose this wedge of land. It seems that it was abandoned, even forgotten, and today is simply a tangle of woody growth. But that is not the whole story.

On my usual journey to the wood, the Tanglewood part is what is first seen in the distance on turning left at the high, exposed crossroads on Waltham Lane. At least it would be if it was more properly woodland and so more conspicuous, since it is the beech trees of Northdown Plantation behind it that are much taller and prominent and catch the eye. Tanglewood's contribution is a loosely hung curtain of clematis strung along this northern edge. The view from the crossroads doesn't last because the lane very gently descends and because of a hedge on the left. Once or twice through gaps in the hedge the fine oaks of Nain's copse beyond Thirlstrup's field are glimpsed, but Tanglewood is lost from view. And, since it is only the tip of the spear shaped triangle of land that meets the lane, by the time the top corner of the wood is reached, where a large, spreading, rather squat sycamore stands sentinel, the bulk of Tanglewood is obscured. Unless there is a reason to visit, in obscurity it remains. With much else to do, it is a case of out of sight out of mind, but that is not quite the whole story either.

A visit to Tanglewood is unlike a visit to any other part of the wood. You cannot walk straight through it but must duck and weave to avoid tough unyielding stems, seeming to grow in every direction but upwards, and to avoid thick lianas and temperate climbers. Dense thorn-infested bushes and briers introduce further detours. Rarely can you walk upright. Rather, head bowed, but eyes ever alert for the next obstacle or obstruction, progress is slow. Sometimes you have to push your way through the tangle, branches scrape your coat, dangling twigs and the fearsome cords of wild rose barbed with precisely spaced thorns scratch your head or dislodge your hat. Every so often a cobweb invisibly wipes your face as you walk into the spider's trap set for far, far smaller prey: you feel the gossamer but don't see it, you wipe it away but the unpleasant sensation lingers. In places the floor is painted green with moss that cloaks long fallen logs revealed only by their roundness and length looking like a miniature long barrow and seemingly as old. It's quite dark too and, like groping in the attic, you eventually emerge into better light, find you are somewhat grubby but are pleased at last to straighten up. The Tanglewood experience is different from wandering among the beeches of Northdown Plantation, or navigating through the young vigorous stems of Taid's Wood or loitering among the older almost ancient woodland of Nain's Copse. But that too is still not quite the whole story.

Tanglewood seems to be what arises when land is neglected to await the fate dealt by the complex interplay of climate, soil, and local vegetation. Arrival of new seeds by wind, birds and animals will slowly add new botanical opportunities and browsing and grazing by rabbits, deer and other hungry herbivores will further influence what develops. Aerial photographs of the 1960s show it as patchy with a hedge running the length of the northern boundary and numerous thicket clumps interspersed by open ground, though years earlier it was doubtless the other way round. Today, it is 'woodland' dominated by hawthorn, blackthorn, some hazel, scattered birches, sallows, a few struggling, unkempt privet bushes, a couple of field maples, and the odd whitebeam, oak, and spindle tree. Really a medley, but none is higher in stature than about 40 or 50 feet (15 metres) and most much shorter. Inevitably on the chalky soils, and because Tanglewood has never been managed, many shrubs and trees are woven together by ropes of lime-loving wild clematis, while briers, the occasional honeysuckle and the fragrant wild rose add to the tangle. In a couple of places calf-thick stems of clematis sitting hydra-like count off the many years since they were cut back, if they ever were. But Tanglewood does boast the best displays of primroses anywhere in the wood, and can also boast (if that is the right word) the greatest number of rabbit burrows, many of which occupy our only badger sett, albeit abandoned by brock well before our time. Since 1996 it boasts on its edge the new pond. But even all of this is not quite the whole story.

Tanglewood's contribution to the wood is more than itself or its parts. It is the wildest area, in a way our 'set aside land'. Its very nature adds to the wood extra dimensions of species, of stature, of structure, of ages, and of infrequency of interference, that together enhance what ecologists call biological diversity, usually contracted to the shorthand 'biodiversity'. It offers a different habitat from anywhere else. While calling it a nature reserve would be exaggeration, the presence of Tanglewood is a wildlife asset enriching the woodland. This is true, and not just an excuse for continued neglect! Proving this is the case is harder. Several friends have helped to evaluate the woodland's wildlife and, more often than not, during such visits assaying animal, plant and bird life spend a disproportionate amount of time in Tanglewood or at its edge. Tanglewood's story is part of the wood's story.

Two sets of friends, botanists Pam and Della Watts and ornithologists Roy Dimmock and Matthew Shaft, have each made several visits in recent years and recorded what they found. Their lists are quite long but neither would claim completeness; indeed, they

have not attempted systematic recording through the four seasons, but these extra eyes and ears, focused and tuned by specialist knowledge, have added immensely to the inventory. Of particular interest has been finding moschatel, the quaint aptly named 'clock-tower plant' with its cubic-faced flowers (incidentally discovered by John White, the book's illustrator), the delicate lilac of lady's smock—properly called 'cuckoo flower' according to Richard Mabey in his splendid Flora Britannica—that my mother delighted to see, Solomon's seal, an alkaline specialist (calcicole) confined to Hampshire and Wiltshire, and the uncommon and similarly chalk-loving long-stalked crane's-bill discovered when Alton's natural history society visited and found it where the open day route emerges from Taid's Wood onto the bottom track.

The false oxlips continue to thrive with a fourth clump discovered near a woodpile and at quite a distance from the three on the track that runs inside the northern edge of Nain's Copse. Several sprays of male fern have appeared in both Nain's Copse and Taid's Wood. I can't recall any clumps in the wood five or six years ago. Their furry bright brown fronds curled tight in May like a paper

Male fern

party whistle are unmistakeable as are the unfurled knee-high pinnate fronds in July. At my childhood home in Petts Wood there was a clump under a remnant patch of woodland birches at the bottom of the garden which probably explains the affection for this flowerless, foliage-rich pteridophyte. Besides the ubiquitous bracken (which the wood does not have despite it being more widely distributed around the world than any other plant) Britain has several wild species of fern. None achieves the tree stature common in the tropics and antipodes, but the ferns augment the feel of a wood—ancient, shaded, leafy green, and damp. Bluebells in Nain's Copse are expanding little by little despite annual browsing by deer, though there is no doubt that their first choice are the few patches of new bluebells added from gifts of bulbs. The long established patches under the old oaks on the northern boundary mostly escape all but a cursory nibbling, while the clump no more than 10 m away growing up from a gift from Stephen and Margaret West is devoured each year, the succulent leaves sheared almost to ground level.

Less successful has been the slow recovery of primroses on the cross-rides that were crushed, squashed and squelched during timber harvesting in April 1992. They are still there, but no longer such an arresting display in Spring. The tracked timber harvester badly damaged the tender plants themselves and, because the weather had been wet, compacted the damp soil in the ride where they grow. Together this two-pronged assault was too much and the rosettes of leaves remain dwarfed. Another reason has kept them suppressed. In the early years of ownership John and I tackled the enormous rabbit population, largely bringing it under control by the early 1990s. This led to a change in grass composition throughout the wood, but especially on the rides. Fine grasses of putting green quality, shorn by nature's furry four-legged mowers, were gradually replaced by coarser, taller growing varieties and wood sedge. These tougher types now overtop primrose leaves, shading them in the crucial weeks after flowering when reserves needed rebuilding before the woodland canopy reaches full leaf and casts its dense sunlight-eclipsing shade. And, as the tough grasses turn yellow and die back in summer the blades collapse and overlay the primroses as an unwelcome mulch adding to their struggles. Also, while succulent primrose is not to rabbit's liking, they are delicious to deer, to roe and especially to muntjac. Often the primroses and the wood's

few cowslips are scalloped with precision by these hungry ungulates to leave a saucer of green devoid of the tasty flower buds.

Stinging nettles continue to spread and clematis continues to entangle. Overall, greater observation, the passage of time and increasing familiarity have added to and not subtracted from the wood's wildlife interest.

The arrival of buzzards in the area, the ornithological equivalent of Africa's big cats, excites and interests. When we bought Northdown Plantation in 1985 they were scarce or even absent: today a buzzard, harried by gulls or others on the wing equally anxious of its roaming presence, is a common sight. Usually high overhead, but occasionally gliding with wings flapping languorously just above the tree tops, these great birds of prey signal their arrival crying their eerie 'peeouw'. Very occasionally these majestic eagle-eyed hunters of the air are themselves caught out. Mavis, a friend from church, Margaret and I were enjoying a picnic on the edge of the wildlife glade that is close to Railtrack's electrical substation though well screened from it. We were facing south to catch what warmth the sun could offer on a rather cool early May bank holiday Monday, and so sat looking towards the bottom track. We were not alone in examining it: a buzzard was too, though neither knew it.

Tracking just above the tops of the well-grown ash to its left in

Buzzard

Taid's Wood, the great bird meandered languidly northwards following the open corridor and curves of the track below. The brown be-speckled hawk eyed the track's ruts, tufts of grass and adjacent undergrowth for a hint of movement of vole, wood mouse or shrew. As it neared the grey substation shrouded by overgrown hazel, the picnickers were still, momentarily, out of sight. One more effortless beat of the wings and suddenly, sharply, and only 20 feet away were three humans. Startled, the enormous bird wheeled round, as if pivoting on its wing tip, and soared aloft and away. It was gone in a trice, or almost so for it flew around the wood once or twice eyeing us from a distance before it was gone. But captured in our minds are the great wings perfected for such manoeuvres, taught, and spanning every inch of their three feet with pinions open-slotted like fingers outstretched: it was the moment the observer became the observed. The predator had been seen, its prey had gained a lease of life, and three picnickers were fleetingly entertained by absolute natural theatre.

Drama is uncommon; the gentle unfolding of nature's daily delights is not. Amongst the best is to watch a flock of long-tailed tits, a dozen or more with their tiny round pinkish bodies attached to long black and white tails, flit through the branches from one tree to the next. They move as a group but without synchronism, always individuals but always aware of what the others are doing, a little community passing through the wood. They progress just like the sleek highly strung impala of southern Africa's bush and also like them, with their dainty, fickle diets taking a bite here and a mouthful there, the tits seem to stay barely long enough to garner a grub or ingest a beetle. They are like casual shoppers at market, not intent on a single deliberate purchase, but trying this and trying that, examining here and inspecting there. Unlike shoppers, but not unlike Africa's adorable impala, the little long-tailed tits are a joy to watch again and again.

As for birdsong, I am poor at distinguishing (or is it remembering?) the different notes and tunes. My father was so good at it, always telling us what this or that bird was, but I was lazy and uninterested at the time and never bothered to learn. How often children take their parents' wisdom too much for granted and come to regret not attending more to their abilities and gifts. Thus it was only when Matthew and Roy made their first visit to the wood that I learnt of their surprise on hearing so many wrens defending so many territories in just one 30-acre patch: my untutored ear hadn't detected anything unusual. Their visit was in the spring after the beech had been thinned in the winter of 1997/98 and apparently the piles of branches left from the operation were ideal habitat for nesting for this tiniest, but certainly not quietest, of Britain's birds, hence their proliferation. Some song is memorable, or made so by a supercilious mnemonic like the oft-repeated call of the wood pigeon 'My toes hurt, Betty; my toes hurt, Betty'; and so on, and always finishing plaintively but abruptly on a rising ... 'my' as if suddenly discovering no one, least of all Betty, is listening.

Observing the rhythm of woodland life and its phenology has revealed how late the Douglas firs flush in Spring, sometimes it is not until June that the new fresh green shoots extend from the swollen buds. In early May, beneath the beech trees, a gentle rain of leaf bud scales, bright brown, translucent and tissue thin, falls from the canopy over several days as every single steadily swelling bud casts them off. Every receptacle and every object brought for our first open day, on 6th May 1996, were blessed with this arboreal confetti! In autumn the unhurried and often late turning of beech to their bronze and burnt tints contrasts with the sudden defoliation ash suffers with barely a colour change before the first frost sees off the leaves. The rhythm seems delayed in winter when hopeful searches for snowdrops in the only patch in the wood beside Railtrack's electrical substation, always disappoint until mid-February, long after others in churchyards and front gardens have announced spring's imminence.

We have taken several steps to enrich wildlife habitat. Very obviously the small pond has brought water, and a little transposing of primroses has been equally direct. Sowing wildflower seed has brought indifferent results, planting bluebell bulbs did not go unnoticed by the wood's ungulates, while the introduction of wild garlic, that loveliest and most aromatic of spring adornments, is still in its early days. Two glades have been cut to add structure, a warm corner, and a new picnic site, but have been quickly invaded by coarse grasses rather than encouraging the splash of primroses. Dead wood is left, deliberately and in desultory fashion for borers, beetles and other bite-size beasts of decay. Importantly, regular thinning keeps stands open and light to the forest floor and some limiting coppicing of hazel has rejuvenated several stools. Also no pesticide has been used in the wood for over ten years, and then it was only a mild herbicide controlling weeds around the trees in

Taid's Wood which make up only about a tenth of the area. And finally there is Tanglewood, and Tanglewood will stay as Tanglewood.

Long-stalked crane's-bill

15

Cleaning Taid's Wood

In 1987 my brother-in-law and I planted four acres of new wood-land beside the railway. We had acquired access to land that hadn't been expected until 2003, and together we planted it with a mixture of ash, wild cherry and oak. The trees grew vigorously in their early years with each individually protected by the then latest device, the plastic tubes or treeshelters known as Tuley tubes after their inventor, that today litter so much of our countryside. The treeshelters worked well; hardly any trees died, and along with attention to weeding many grew almost one metre in height each year. The ash and cherry were almost neck and neck making a creditable 8 metres or so by 10 years of age. The oaks were not far behind reaching almost 6 metres in this time. Each year the average height of the best trees was measured to obtain a statistic that English foresters know as 'top height'. It isn't at all necessary to measure trees so frequently, but as my first large planting was a planting of traditional broadleaves on which I am supposed to be an authority, pride demanded to know how well they were doing. The four acres were well stocked and, excepting the odd poorer patch, the oak, ash and wild cherry were all at the upper end of expected growth rate for the site Taid's Wood is: sheltered, with a thinnish loam soil over chalk rubble.

After weeding was finished, once it was no longer necessary to kill the young trees' competitors for moisture and nutrients such as grass and bramble, visits to Taid's Wood diminished. But it was only a little while later that some of the trees in their shelters were outgrowing their plastic kindergarten and trying to force apart the unyielding tubes. Several of the cherries were killed at this stage, the grip of the tube seeming, in an unscientific sense, to throttle them like a ligature. The ash did not suffer badly, though if tubes were left on too long enclosing wet, often airless, conditions, the suffocating stem became slimy and covered with white excrescences or pustules where cells in the bark multiplied in a desperate attempt to help the bark to breath. Oaks were not killed, though their bark did sometimes show these white eruptions, probably because the trees grew more slowly. By the time the plastic treeshelters were removed from all the trees many oaks had still not grown to fully fill the tubes.

Treeshelter removal had not been intended as an establishment operation. The plastic tubes were supposed to decay in sunlight after about five or six years, but the Tubex ones used were an early design and even after ten years showed few signs of weakening, let alone breaking down. The plastic contained too much ultraviolet inhibitor while the shelter itself was shaded from direct sunlight after the second or third year by the very tree it protected. Removal of shelters was the only recourse, and it was a two stage operation.

When the trees were seven or eight years old the shelters were slit almost to the top, a bit like a woman's deeply slit skirt that remains fully intact around the buttocks and waist, though revealed in Taid's Wood was rough bark not shapely flesh! The partial slitting released the enclosed stem, sometimes cascading water trapped as if from a blocked drainpipe, but still provided the tender tree some protection from rabbits gnawing the bark, and from deer using it as stock for fraying their antlers. Two or three years later the shelter was finally removed by slitting the last few inches at the top and the whole thing 'peeled' from its tree like having a plaster cast removed from a broken limb. Unlike a plaster cast the plastic treeshelter curled back to its original tubular shape because of what plastics technologists call 'memory', or a tendency to return to the shape in which it was first formed. For some of the fastest growing cherry trees the operations were done as early as five years, with complete removal before age eight years. Slitting was effected by a Stanley knife or hardened steel Swedish foresters knife given to me by a visiting colleague, and needed to be almost surgical in precision. The critical issue was not the tool but how it was handled. The double walled plastic used by Tubex could not simply be slit by holding the knife perpendicular to the tree. The knife held that way invariably cut too deeply, scouring the bark which had no wadding to protect it, unlike a person's limb inside a plaster when subjected to a similarly tricky removal operation. However, by holding the knife tangentially and using it to lift the plastic ever so slightly as it cut, scouring and damaging incisions were mostly avoided.

Sporadic removal of treeshelters began in the mid-1990s as the cherry trees quickly swelled to fill the tubes. Removal of all of them from Taid's Wood began in January 1999 in the smaller southerly portion. I was helped by my brother-in-law, John: he removed the shelters and I used long-arm pruners to cut large side branches or to single forked trees and generally to improve stem form. A few weeks later students from Imperial College spent a day in the wood, ostensibly to learn woodland ecology and silvi-culture, and completed treeshelter removal from this part of the wood. They were shown how to prune a tree correctly, but unlike ecology and management, not a lot was learnt as the pegs, scars and abraded bark testified. Still, there's nothing like real practical work for experience.

In the larger northern part of Taid's Wood treeshelter removal began by Mike Fisher, my neighbour, helping himself to about 300 for his own tree planting, and was completed by friends of Dr Everett on their winter visits to the wood in the late 1990s. The unwanted shelters themselves were re-nested and piled up, and are still in Taid's Wood. They are becoming overgrown, and some of the tubes have doubtless become home to snails and perhaps the odd mouse or even a wren's nest. How finally to dispose of them is an open question. Their flesh coloured plastic seems as tough as ever.

Once de-sheltering was complete, Taid's Wood was again neglected. Some singling of forked stems and high pruning of wild cherry trees occupied occasional Saturday mornings, but there was no other substantial improvement work for a couple of years. For many well-established plantations little attention is needed until they are 20 or more years old when a first thinning takes place. As a result such plantations can get forgotten. And this neglect can be damaging for broadleaved stands like ours. Unlike most conifers and trees such as poplars, species like oak, beech, and ash often fail to develop a straight stem unless deliberately helped to do so by the way the trees are grown and cared for. Straight stems are encouraged by growing trees close together, to force upward height and suppress heavy side branches by mutual shading, by selecting trees of good genetic stock, or by deliberate formative pruning. In the case of Taid's Wood, although we had planted the trees at a separation of eight to ten feet, using coppice growth of sycamore and some hazel did, in several places, provide the more densely stocked conditions. But using other woody growth in this way runs the risk that it will dominate, and even suppress, the favoured trees. Indeed, any vigorous woody growth can do this. It's like allowing moss to green up bare patches of lawn only to find it takes over everywhere. Thus a time usually comes when a stand of trees needs sorting out, and the job is called 'cleaning'. Cleaning brings in no cash but lays the foundation for the future crop. With broadleaves it is a job neglected at peril. In Taid's Wood serious cleaning began in the winter of 2000 when the trees had completed 14 growing seasons. The best ash and cherry were 11–12 metres tall and the oak about 8–9 metres. Beginning with the larger northern block everything was finished by the end of January before bird nesting began in earnest: young stands with much undergrowth and debris, not to mention the inevitable tangle of *Clematis* on the chalky soils, provide numerous nesting sites for wrens, robins and warblers.

Cleaning began at the end of Taid's Wood near the two conservation glades students had helped clear a year before. Initially, one is hesitant deciding what to cut, but over several half days, six distinct activities evolved. It was like tidying the garage, the more one does the more is discovered that needs attention and the whole job takes longer than intended though, with perseverance, the final result can be most satisfying. The main cleaning task in Taid's Wood was to cut coppice regrowth of sycamore and hazel and other woody species that had sprung up from self-sown seed, such as birch and sallow, that competed with the planted ash, oak and cherry trees. My small Stihl chainsaw, lightweight with a short 12 inch drawbar, proved ideal. Stem thickness rarely exceeded 3 inches and with a well-sharpened chain the saw cut through in seconds. A heavy-duty clearing saw would have been just as suitable. With head down and felling several coppice stems in quick succession a rhythm develops but at the risk of being overzealous. Not only is there the question of safety, but not every unplanned

Old man's beard (Clematis vitalba)

and unplanted woody stem is necessarily unwanted. With the relatively widely spaced trees there was still benefit to be had from extra stems to make good any gaps for a few years more and, in a few places, actually to substitute the planted tree if it had failed or was growing badly. It was important continually to keep an eye on the surrounding trees where one worked and always be on the look out to recruit a new stem. In several spots well-grown sycamores were added in this way. The grand object was to secure the future of all the best trees and sometimes bring into the reckoning a new one. By cleaning, an unmanageable thicket was transformed into a young stand of forest trees.

On most days when working through Taid's Wood a robin arrived for company. It perched a few feet away on freshly cut stems only to fly off if work momentarily stopped. But it seemed to like company and relished the morsels that disturbance yielded. Robins find human activity congenial and can become quite tame. Indeed the friendly robin in Taid's Wood reminded me of my father, Taid himself. Taid, Welsh for grandfather and hence Taid to our boys, for many years fed robins with meal worms in our back

135

garden in Petts Wood where I grew up. With care he would entice the nervous bird to take the wriggling morsel from his fingers. My father was a careful ornithologist and over several years closely observed our garden robins, their territorial battles, and their success or otherwise nesting in a box on an oak tree. He recorded it all and wrote the graphic story, a copy of which I have, with its awful conclusion of utter destruction of the clutch of 1956. It was good to be reminded of father as the woodland named in his honour was cleaned.

A few of the planted trees, while healthy and growing vigorously, had such poorly shaped stems that bent, twisted or forked badly or had such ungainly crowns of branches that no amount of

BIRD TABLE

My father's robin sketch

formative pruning would produce anything worthwhile. These 'wolf' trees are best cut out during cleaning or at first thinning at the latest. If not, they occupy much space and interfere with better formed adjacent trees. This operation is aptly called 'de-wolfing'— sounds a candidate word for BBC's 'Call my Bluff'! Perhaps 1 ash in 20 was culled from Taid's Wood for this reason and 1 in 50 of the generally better formed cherry trees. Also, occasionally an ash was cut if it showed signs of canker. None of the oaks was really big enough to merit the de-wolfing epithet and also they were being grown in a different way from the rest of stand.

Tiny groups of oaks had been scattered throughout the matrix of ash and cherry trees at 14 metre centres with the intention that oak will ultimately form the final crop. At each centre three oak trees were planted in a triangle very close together with the idea of selecting the best. A choice of one out of three for oak with its generally poor form is barely sufficient. In many mixed stands of this kind the forester plants groups of five, or more commonly nine, and sometimes even sixteen from which to make the eventual choice. I hoped to get away with just three at each centre because the acorns had come from good genetic stock and the very activity being described had been factored in, namely formative pruning at the right time. Assuming I was around this wood at least would not be neglected! As cleaning of Taid's Wood proceeded the triplets of oak were inspected and one or even two of the trees cut if there was already a clear winner developing with good form and vigour. However, for a couple of the groups it was already too late. All three oak trees with their slower growth were dead or nearly so, suppressed by vigorous adjacent ash trees or sycamore coppice. A couple more threesomes had no oaks showing any promise. Silviculturally, it was asking a lot for one out of just three to have some potential in every case. Where groups were dead, or just too poor to do anything with, the long-term future of the stand at that location was switched to relying on a good neighbouring ash instead.

All the while cleaning proceeded the job was repeatedly interrupted by the strings and ropes of *Clematis* that entangled the undergrowth and ascended into the crowns. Sometimes they stretched from tree to tree like rigging on a sailing ship, but without the order and purpose, and would prevent cut stems falling to the ground. The problem was not serious, since during establishment of Taid's Wood cutting and killing *Clematis* had been a priority. There are numerous much worse thicket stage wood-lands on the chalk and limestone hills of southeast England quite overwhelmed by this temperate vine. Nevertheless, dealing with it was a crucial part of the cleaning. Tough stems, an inch across, were cut near the base and, importantly, the climber itself was pulled down from every tree it had assaulted. This proved easier than our struggles over a decade earlier with older and thicker *Clematis* that entwined so many of the beech trees when we first bought Northdown Plantation in 1985. And on one wintertime cleaning visit to Taid's Wood, it was almost fun. Ben, our youngest son, was back from his first term at Exeter University, and had come to help and took on the climber pulling task. It was the Saturday before New Year when most of the country was still in the grip of snow and ice. The trees in Taid's Wood were not only gripped by *Clematis* but still, albeit loosely, by Wednesday night's snow. Cutting any woody growth with the chainsaw sprinkled snow but Ben, yanking and pulling down *Clematis*, sometimes with all the strength he could muster, repeatedly got thoroughly showered. But at least the snow did lubricate the branches so that the whole tangled mass slid off the tree quite readily. On one occa-sion everything, except for one thick strand, fell down, coiled itself at the base, and looked like a snake charmer's python. As we worked, cutting with the chainsaw and tugging at *Clematis*, and then tidying everything up, we kept warm and the dousings of snow hardly mattered.

The final cleaning task, having opened up the stand and favoured the better trees, was to revisit each one for singling and pruning. While the few really ungainly 'wolf' trees were felled, many ash and a few of the wild cherry were forked or had heavy branches that caused their crowns to interfere with less vigorous but frequently better formed neighbours. It was necessary to work through the stand cutting off these unwanted limbs. Although the offending limbs were often rather large—ideally pruning should be confined to branches less than 2 inches across—removing them did give room for adjacent trees to develop. When the first proper thinning takes place in a few years time the future of these par-tially de-limbed trees will be reconsidered, and many will proba-bly go from the stand. As with thinning, the intensity of cleaning and what is removed is an open question. More thorough cleaning and removal of the poorer trees would make an already low stocked stand decidedly gappy and moth-eaten in appearance.

Time will tell. As with most forestry tasks today's handiwork will be judged many years into the future.

16

The badger incident

In Tanglewood, the spear-shaped triangle of undergrowth, scrub, and assorted trees on the northwest edge of the wood is the remnants of a badger sett. It is where one might be expected, just inside woodland adjacent to farmland, but in our time it has only been occupied by leporid proprietors; rabbits must find long abandoned sets an easy dig. Our soils of chalk rubble must be difficult to burrow, but once turned over by badgers excavations and runs become altogether more malleable. Intensive rabbit clearance efforts have diminished since the appalling numbers bequeathed us in the mid-1980s, but a few active burrows have reappeared with the most notable being in this old badger sett.

Badgers are much in the news as numbers have increased for this protected species and because of the still unresolved question of whether or not they infect cattle with tuberculosis (TB). Farmers have had so much to cope with in recent years that rising TB levels seem like a last straw. The increases in outbreaks correlate with increasing badger numbers. Yet the concrete scientific proof, proof more than correlation alone, that badgers are the main source of infection remains elusive and resort is made to region wide experiments comparing clearance with non-clearance of badgers from farmland. Fortunately trees don't catch TB, but the rise and spread of brock the badger has reached the borders of the wood.

In April 2000 the wood was readied for a Millennium open day planned for May 1st. One particular afternoon's job was to check the open day route. While at the farthest stop in Nain's copse, our neighbour, Alan Purkiss, was noisily busy in his adjoining wood. He was burning debris accumulated from his local tree work and as we got talking he described finding an almost fresh badger carcass two days before on our side of the railway embankment. He thought the animal must have been electrocuted: our line has the 'third rail' so much beloved in the south of England and not the overhead gantry system common elsewhere. This incident showed that badgers were in the area, although in 16 years ownership of Northdown Plantation none had been seen. Alan's badger intelligence was mentally filed away and noted in my woodland 'diary'. That afternoon he also helped rediscover the 'lost' false oxlip close to our common boundary. Before finishing that day, several rosettes of primroses were carefully prised up from the middle of the open day trail route, where it leaves the main track, and transplanted to a safer spot in a newly cleared wildlife glade near Railtrack's grey electrical substation.

The next visit was five days later, on Easter Monday, and with under a week to go before the open day. Several new posts for the displays were installed where the old ones had rotted. The entire trail route was checked to ensure it was easy to follow. As usual at stop 4 the crude 'A' frame was erected to hold the spring scale for weighing the seasoned and unseasoned logs; an activity youngsters have such fun with as they learn that heavy logs are wet logs and no good for burning. The job took about three-quarters of an hour to assemble the Heath-Robinson apparatus, but in the end it was functional. While working on stop 4, which is only about 10 metres from the railway line, an awful smell, suddenly wafted past. Perhaps the wind shifted while at work and what had not been noticeable initially now assailed the nostrils. The nose led the way to investigate.

About 25 metres away and lying on the stone ballast beside the railway track, halfway between the rail itself and Railtrack's five-strand wire fence that runs along the bottom of the wood, lay a dead badger. Looking over the fence the carcass was well bloated, skin was taught and the stench of decaying flesh suggested death had occurred a week or ten days before. There wasn't time to do anything there and then, and anyway poor brock was just out of reach. Clearly, though, things couldn't be left as they were for open day visitors to discover, especially since between stop 4 and the carcass was one of only two designated picnic sites. It was getting late for joining the family, including my eldest son Jon and his delightful and very friendly Norwegian girlfriend, Christina, for lunch at our nearest pub, The Fox, just on the edge of North Waltham village. During the meal I regaled them with the badger incident.

The account of the dead badger was delayed until after the main course and we were waiting for the dessert. How should it be removed? In what way should it be disposed of, or was it all Railtrack's responsibility? The meal's conviviality, and low level of interest in dad's badger problem—none had smelt the smell—led to suggestions that Railtrack should rebuild and re-route the entire London—Southampton line or that we should dig up the whole wood and move it away from the smelly badger, or even plant a new one with genetically modified (GM) trees designed to produce an identical wood by May Day. It was at least agreed that, either we had to get away from the badger or it had to go. More seriously, and urgently in view of how little time there was to the open day, it was clear that a third pre-open day visit to the wood was called for.

That evening I phoned Alan to tell him about this new carcass. He remarked that he had seen a silver grey S registered car at our entrance that afternoon at about 2.35 pm—he had not lost his policing skills despite being retired from the Hampshire Constabulary for several years, and we were grateful for his good neighbourliness. The car was our son's, Jon. Apparently he and Christina had gone to the wood, both for her to see it and perhaps intrigued about the badger after all. Talking to Jon later in the day he was exceedingly curious to know who had spied on him, tracking his movements after we had parted!

On the following Friday it was cool and drizzly in the wood, alternating between mist and light rain. This wasn't too perturbing since Monday's forecast for the open day was improving each time we heard the weatherman. Using a garden spade I dug an 18 inch deep hole under a clump of hazel close to the railway fence. A few exertions didn't produce the desired cavity: I was inexperienced at grave digging and the soil proved gravely and full of coal fragments. It was the place where coal wagons had been unloaded for Steventon manor when a siding existed for a few years in the 1930s in this part of Taid's Wood. Eventually the hole was ready, but like so many things one tackles it took longer than expected.

The badger incident

With spade in hand I squirmed through the flimsy five-strand wire fence and, after carefully listening for distant trains, began the momentary trespass to retrieve the carcass. Prizing up brock with outstretched spade and shuffling him into position to get proper purchase took longer than the intended few seconds. With ears ever alert for trains, nose already sensing the smell, eyes were now drawn to the underside of the carcass to reveal flesh sloughing off and a festering, writhing mass of maggots! I now had to rely on a fourth sense. Slowly I raised the disagreeable and surprisingly heavy corpse and, holding it at arms length, edged back to the fence. Still balancing brock on the spade and with my own torso aching, I squeezed through the parallel wires of the fence, momentarily arabesque like a ballerina, but lacking the required grace and poise since the poor beast fell off. Fortunately this last indignity was now inside the wood and the badger's remains were quickly scooped up and laid to rest in the freshly dug grave. The dark coal-riven earth filled the gaps and the slightly proud mound is now the only sign of the badger's last resting place. If God knows when even a sparrow falls to the ground, it is certainly right that this handsome creature was given a burial.

Encouraging badgers back into the wood, even to resume residence in the abandoned set in Tanglewood, must await its natural course. But return of badgers seems likely now we know they are in the area. And, too, Christina, now my daughter-in-law, knows what her father-in-law sometimes gets up to.

Two years before the badger episode there was a more distressing animal incident. In January 1998, as tidying up after the beech thinning was coming to an end—mainly clearing mud off the lane—high pruning of the Douglas firs was resumed along with some thinning work in Nain's Copse. The Toll family, including Will and Ed, my son Ben's school friends, came to collect some firewood. In the midst of felling a small sycamore Mr Toll suddenly

143

appeared striding towards me, shouting over the scream of the chainsaw. Interrupting the cutting he yelled that two brown and black striped dogs had been racing around and then picked up the scent of a deer and were now harrying it. His sons, Will and Ed, had frantically tried to shoo the dogs away. This was odd. Surely a deer would spring away in a flash with its long legs, easily outrunning and outjumping dogs? We hastened to where the excitement was. Lying beneath an old clump of hazel, not far from the pond and near to the abandoned badger sett in Tanglewood, was a roe deer buck looking forlorn, nervous of our presence, but evidently still alive. We approached cautiously and were fixed by a pair of large doleful eyes, hiding fear and surely pain as this creature, already terrified by the howling and snapping dogs, was clearly unable to move. It was breathing heavily and blood seeped from the corner of its mouth. There were many tufts of fur, doubtless from the fight with the dogs, which Will later described as 'nothing like he had ever seen'. The scene was distressing.

The roe deer was in a bad shape, although it wasn't obvious where it was hurt. The pain threshold of roe is remarkably high. Trials of the efficacy of electric fencing have shown that roe deer can tolerate 500 times the level of shock that either humans or, for that matter, red deer can. The thick skin and fur appear to be more than just good insulation from cold. Roe have been seen approaching a powerfully electrified fence, being initially repulsed by the electric charge, then make several return visits or patrol along its length, get used to it, and then force their way through, despite the 5000 volt pulsating current, to emerge unscathed. If roe can put up with this, what had so distressed the animal before us?

The dogs, now firmly on leads, were led back to Northdown Orchard where they had come from. We decided to leave the scene expecting the deer to recover and eventually move on. It wasn't to be. Mike, my neighbour who owns Northdown Orchard, was concerned and had later visited the spot and found the deer in much the same state; he decided to call the RSPCA. On arrival the officer quickly decided to put the animal out of its misery, and it was then taken away. Inspection of the carcass suggested that it had been struck by a vehicle and, while outward breakages were little in evidence, the deer had probably suffered internal damage to organs, massive bleeding and other harm. The poor beast had doubtless dragged itself into the wood, and sought out a quiet spot to end its days, perhaps attracted by the pond, gasping with thirst and sorely in need of water to drink. It was then scented by the dogs which, finding it couldn't run, attacked it. And then we found it.

Traffic accidents with deer are commonplace. Indeed, a week before writing this my son Stephen woke me at midnight to say that he had struck a deer on the lane from Bentworth to Alton and that his car's radiator was stoved in and the nearside headlight broken. Fortunately he had managed to reach Pritchard's, Alton's accident repair garage, and the cost of putting everything straight was not too high. Fortunately too the deer appears to have been killed instantly, since our son's friend, also a Stephen, managed to drag the carcass off the road into the woodland from where the animal had sprung so unannounced, and to such harm to itself and the car. The Department of Transport report hundreds of accidents with deer every year. Deer populations continue to increase, a feature of almost all ungulates across the temperate world, and one which baffles ecologists, and so accidents are increasingly likely. One deterrent is to place at intervals tiny reflectors about 20 metres inside a woodland or forest so that at night, when accidents usually occur, headlights from cars flash lights into the wood and scare or warn deer away from the highway. But such measures can't be in place everywhere. Drivers in the countryside must just try to be as cautious as possible.

We were sad to hear of the death of this lovely creature. But there is one species of deer whose numbers need to be reduced substantially—the muntjac. This deer species, like the grey squirrel, is not native to our shores. It was introduced from China early in the 20th century, initially into Bedfordshire, for amusement, entertainment, even scientific interest, but subsequently escaped and found our climate and countryside congenial. Muntjacs are small, secretive and rarely seen. Their numbers are multiplying rapidly and most woodlands in East Anglia and increasingly in southern England and the midlands have resident populations. They are a scourge not just because they are exotic—after all so are potatoes and wheat—but because they devour foliage and flowers of herbaceous plants. Put bluntly, unlike our three native deer species, they preferentially consume wild flowers—almost, it seems, the rarer the better. English Nature are seriously concerned at the devastation muntjac cause in nature reserves, especially those designated to protect rare plants. Controlling them is proving nearly impossible. They hide in undergrowth, are no bigger than a terrier, and are extremely wary of humans. They are resourceful and will damage young coppice shoots by nipping them in the stem to bend them down to reach the succulent foliage. If this doesn't work they will even walk into a clump of coppice and use their weight to bend down a supple stem and run it through their mouths, rather like finishing a kebab, to strip out the leaves. And, while they do not strip bark like other deer species, they will, like fallow deer, fray plastic treeshelters. Somehow the muntjac population must be contained or England's wild flowers will suffer irreparably.

One muntjac has been spotted in the wood. It was among the young trees of Taid's Wood, presenting no more than a fleeting glimpse of the hindquarters of a deer-like animal that looked no bigger than a whippet retreating in to the undergrowth. Also observed, by way of corroboration, is increasing browsing of blue-bells in the spring, especially newly introduced ones likes those the Wests kindly gave us, and primroses, cowslips and even the rare false oxlips, suffering bite-size mouthfuls scalloped from their soft centres. None of this is proof positive that muntjacs are the culprit, but it wouldn't be a surprise. Brenda Mayle, a Forestry Commission's deer expert, actually illustrates her booklet about managing deer in the countryside with two photographs of muntjac damage, namely the heart of an oxlip eaten right out and bluebells shorn of flowers. She sums up the problem with the understatement 'they feed selectively on important woodland flowers'!

This chapter won't only dwell on sombre thoughts of the dead, the dying or the destructive, because in August 1998 there was a fox incident as memorable as any already related—and I don't mean the discovery of our nearest pub! It was on the day that involves going right round the wood to empty bait and gather up the hoppers used in squirrel control. It's not a particularly pleasant job since often the bait has become congealed and needs digging out, or sometimes it is a bit mouldy, or even on occasion it has started to sprout, especially if the hopper is sited on the ground and the bait has got damp. Clearing up the bait and removing the hoppers has to be done in early August to comply with the law that forbids grey squirrel control using warfarin poison after the 15th of the month. The job brings to an end that season's control and the concomitant regular visits and, if control has been effective, there is the satisfaction of saving the beech trees for one more year from having their bark torn off: but, enough of gloomy thoughts.

When walking back through the 40-year-old beech trees on the north side of Northdown Plantation one group of trees looked prematurely bronzed in the crown. It was too early for autumn colouring but looking up into the crowns revealed little of the cause. On looking down though I spied a fox about 30 metres away and it hadn't spied me nor picked up my scent as I was downwind from it. Its coat was a rich red-brown, foxy red as you would expect. As I watched it, standing as still as possible with the wire handles of metal squirrel hoppers cutting into my fingers, the fox proceeded on its journey oblivious of an audience. It was making its way up through the wood towards the lane but, all the time, kept bearing a little to its right so that it traced an arc of radius 30 metres from where I stood. It remained in sight for what seemed several minutes.

It was a wary fox and every so often would stop, look and sniff the air. I remained undetected and it proceeded on. As it did so, tracing a steady tack to leeward around me, to borrow a maritime analogy, it kept making little jumps. One moment all was visible, the next all was hidden except for the tips of its ears, then it would bob up in the open, as if on the crest of wave, and then again be lost from sight. It was negotiating the debris of the previous winter's beech thinning. To press the analogy it was like the rise and fall of a dolphin swimming in the sea, though in this case it was the lush green sea of dog's mercury. I was transfixed, only putting down the now painful hoppers once the fox was lost from sight and still oblivious of its observer. The scene was one to relish: to observe and not be observed.

This wasn't the first encounter with a fox in the wood. From time to time one catches their unmistakable smell, usually fleetingly but characteristic enough once recognized. Also in our early days of ownership, when we tackled systematically and with determination the massive numbers of rabbits inhabiting no fewer than 16 different warrens across our original 22-acre patch, we inadvertently blocked up and gassed a fox's earth. From time to time feathers betray a successful hunt, though whether it is a fox's prey or that of buzzard or sparrowhawk is not always clear. It's just a pity that foxes are not skilled tree climbers able to hunt grey squirrels; even their flying namesakes—the fruit bats—are no use for this, being both tropical and vegetarian. Grey squirrels need a predator.

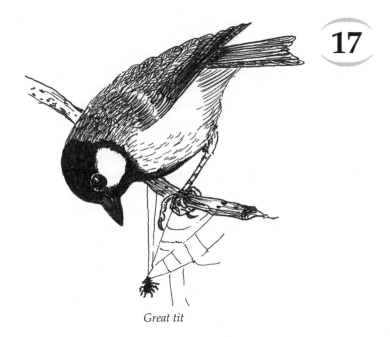

17

Great tit

The menace of the greys

The best and worst welcoming parties were there. It was the day before Christmas Eve 2000 and by the time the car had climbed to the cross roads on Waltham Lane on the last part of the journey, the grey, interminably overcast sky had become an enveloping mist. The wood could not be made out. Its northwest corner, usually so sharp against the skyline, only emerged in the last 100 yards when more or less level with the telephone pole often frequented by a yellowhammer. At the entrance all was dull and dank with a gentle dripping from the overhanging branches shedding their condensate of mid-winter damp. And there was a grey squirrel negotiating an ivy-clad beech to the left of the gate—an unwelcome sight of an unwelcome pest. Only a few weeks before, on three occasions, a multi-catch trap had been set and it caught nothing. These gloomy thoughts were arrested by a handsome great tit that momentarily eyed me from a twig just beyond the passenger side of the car. Its jet black bib bisecting the bright yellow breast seemed to accentuate the brilliance of its plumage when all else was so grey and colourless. Birdlife is one of the joys of the wood; the great tit was the best of welcomes.

The moment was gone and attention returned to the squirrel. It was now crawling along a branch and then leapt high overhead to the large beech to the right of the entrance liberating a shower of drips as it did so. It was this that diverted attention from the great tit. The arboreal pest continued to move through the crowns of beech trees, and the remnant Douglas firs left near the lane, in a southerly direction shaking off little showers as its calling card for every jump. The day was so still that one could hear the showers gradually become fainter and fainter. Clearly though, as if more evidence was needed besides the many fresh dreys, grey squirrels were in the wood. The heavy mast of that autumn meant that the squirrel menace was likely to be appalling in 2001.

Squirrels strip bark from many kinds of broadleaved trees. Sycamore and beech suffer most, their thin bark readily peeled off by the sharp incisors, though oak and even pines are sometimes damaged. Bark is stripped rapidly a flake at a time as each jigsaw-size piece is torn off and immediately discarded. There is little evidence that the animal derives nourishment, certainly not fat or carbohydrate though possibly it does get some mineral from the sappy inner bark called phloem. It is known that damage is worst when squirrel numbers are high, that young males are often the culprits, and that the speed of stripping can be breathtaking. Ring barking stems as thick as telegraph poles takes only a minute or two and young trees 20 or 30 feet tall can be stripped from top to bottom almost as quickly as it takes the wretched beast to climb down. It is also known that stripping is a summer activity, almost wholly confined to the period mid-May to late July; that even highly susceptible trees like our beech are only at risk from serious damage in early life from about 10 to 40 or 50 years of age, and that it is often worst just after a stand has been thinned and the remaining trees are growing vigorously. How strippable bark is, like old wallpaper, depends on many things, and squirrels, like experienced decorators, know this. Since we understand some of this lore too, it helps target prevention and control, but the tools available are limited.

The beeches in Northdown Plantation suffered badly from squirrel damage in the three years 1992–1994. This was after the pine had been thinned out, while the trees were in their 30s and at a highly vulnerable age, and before efforts to get on top of the menace had been redoubled. Since then damage has been light and for three years, 1996–1998, none was seen at all, and we thought perhaps the squirrel wars were over. But in 1999 several trees were partially stripped at the base or along branches or at forks in the crown. Damage occurred again in 2000, though happily still not on the scale of earlier in the decade.

Stripping of bark from branches is difficult to see. Not only are they high in the crown, featureless and dark with the backlight of the sky behind them, but damage is usually along the upper surface as the lazy squirrel simply strips what is beneath its forefeet. This zone of debarked branch, like a long thin banana peeled down one side, traps moisture and readily decays. Years later the weakened, hollowed out branch crashes to the ground in some high wind only then to reveal the squirrel's dastardly handiwork, showing what it had literally once got its teeth into. Bark stripping where a branch forks from the trunk is very common since the animal simply sits or reclines comfortably supported and able to give full attention to tearing off flake after flake. The same is true of root spurs when conveniently exposed on the ground. Cover them up or pile brushwood around the base of a tree and usually this will deter the squirrel. Unlike their extraordinary antics in the garden, when no obstacle seems too great an

impediment to deny them reaching food put out for birds, bark stripping is take or leave it activity. If it is easy, do it and do it a lot.

Grey squirrels can be controlled in one of three ways. Their nests, called dreys, can be poked in winter and spring and any discomfited animal shot with a 12 bore from the ground. Occasionally rough shooters will fire directly into a drey but it is ineffectual since the dense sphere of woven leaves and twigs is as good as any flak jacket and often, anyway, the inhabitant is out feeding and the shot simply wasted. Also such work tends to be too early in the season and while numbers may be brought down, squirrels are adept at recolonising woods from adjoining areas. Vulnerable woods need to be squirrel-free between May and July, not in winter or spring. The second way is to catch and kill squirrels by trapping them. Several trap designs are available but all require careful siting, careful pre-baiting and then baiting, and equally careful attention to setting them. Moreover, for reasons of animal welfare, the law requires that once traps are set they must be visited at least once a day. Trapping takes effort and time, to reverse a familiar phrase, and is best used in emergency if widespread stripping damage occurs and squirrel numbers are high. Some drey poking has been done in the wood, though without support of guns, and also some trapping, but it is mostly a third method of control that is used.

One poison only is permitted to control grey squirrels. This is a form of warfarin developed by Forestry Commission researchers in the 1970s that is too weak to harm other wildlife if taken on the odd occasion. It is mixed with whole wheat and the resulting bait, stained port red by an added dye, is fed to grey squirrels from hoppers designed solely for the purpose. The hopper allows a squirrel to feed as much as it wants but in every other detail of its design it prevents all other animals reaching the poison. Current designs are made of square tubes, the same shape as young Stephenson's Menai Straits railway crossing to Anglesey—not every Victorian engineer could bring himself to call it a bridge, and even Stephenson became anxious and added turrets from which to suspend chains. The square tube inside which trains run worked wonderfully for over a century until road builders got to work and put a four lane highway over the top. The similarly profiled steel squirrel hoppers are 'L' shaped. The true hopper part is the upright of the 'L' and holds about a kilogram of bait. It is filled from the top, a job that must be done carefully to avoid spillage, and sealed with a metal lid that fits snugly like a hat. On two sides of the lid are holes through which the wire clip-cum-handle pins it to the hopper. At the bottom of the hopper, bait feeds through a small opening into the horizontal part of the 'L' that is of similar length to the upright but has a small rill or lip a little way along to hold the bait in a sort of tray and prevent it from spilling into the rest of the tube. Just beyond this rill, but still about 20 cm from the opening, is a heavy metal or Perspex flap resting at an angle and sometimes with a magnet to give it added resistance to being prised open. All this paraphernalia is to permit access to the aggressive, inquisitive, strong and indefatigable grey squirrel that delights in dark tunnels and challenges, but denies access to all other animals not possessed of these pugnacious qualities. The hoppers work well and experiments show that bait only ever reaches the intended victim. Indeed, aggressive males have been seen defending 'their' hoppers against other squirrels, so attached are they to them despite the obstacle course! In the wood several of the hoppers have teeth marks on the steel lid where the tenacious animal has sought unsuccessfully to gain further access to the nourishing but deadly bait.

Across Northdown Plantation and Nain's Copse up to eight hoppers are set in place by the end of March. One is lodged on a fallen sycamore log, but the rest are sited at the base of large trees where the ground is open and access to the hopper tunnel unimpeded. Each is angled so that the tunnel slopes down a little to stop rainwater moistening the bait and is pinned to the ground with two wire fence pegs through flanges provided for the purpose. A large log is laid across the hopper to secure it further and additional small ones are added for disguise—to hide it from interference not squirrels. Once in place, the hopper's arrival has to be announced to the squirrel population. Handfuls of whole maize are scattered around its entrance to show it is open for business. Maize attracts squirrels like frying bacon at breakfast time and such pre-baiting need only last about a week. Their inquisitiveness soon has them clambering along the tunnel, thrusting up the heavy flap, and finding the real bait. Normally one hopper for every one to two hectares of vulnerable woodland is sufficient.

Once the hopper has bait it is checked at least weekly to replenish the supply and ensure it is free running. In wet conditions the damp can make the grains of wheat congeal, and even germinate and become unpalatable. Also, despite using one's best skills feeding may simply not take place at a hopper and bait remain uneaten. The hopper might be sited poorly, squirrels may not have found it, or their control is being effected adequately by the others. Such hoppers may be relocated or simply removed. All hoppers are removed at the end of July or early August and unused bait carefully disposed of.

All these efforts appeared to pay off. The years 1996, 1997 and 1998 were damage-free and then in July 1999, as we were packing up after the open day held in aid of Alton's famous heart Rehab programme, six trees near the cross rides had root spurs stripped and many more trees had postage stamp size patches torn out where the wretched animals had tested the bark's stripability. The damage only harmed beech, sycamore seemed unaffected, and was confined to trees where the trunk or root spurs where exposed. If the base of the trees was swathed in dog's mercury or still piled up with the brushwood treatment experimented with a few years before, the bark was intact. Subsequent visits in July revealed further stripping, though confined to trees in the same cross-rides area. My notes say that this was the worst damage seen since the bad years of 1992 and 1993. I was dismayed and professionally annoyed at allowing damage to recur, and cast around for possible causes.

The year 1999 was not particularly bad for squirrel damage according to Harry Pepper, the Forestry Commission's expert, though 1998 had been. However, for Northdown Plantation 1999 was significant because it was the first year when the beech trees would begin to respond vigorously to the thinning carried out in the winter of 1997/98. The extra growing room afforded the remaining trees often only takes effect in the second season after a thinning, and 1999 was this second season. The beech, with more space to grow, will have developed wide annual rings with thick phloem tissue—the layer immediately under the bark—and these were conditions known to render bark more easily peeled off or stripped. Also, in 1998 and 1999 only five hoppers, rather than the usual eight, were used in the wood: the run of the preceding squirrel-free years led to complacency!

After the middle of July no further damage was found. There had been a frenzied attack in late June and that was all. Or so I hoped. Indeed, there was no further stripping that year.

In 2000 I determinedly resumed use of all eight hoppers. But as early as 1st June a couple of beech trees showed patch nibbling. As the month progressed feeding at hoppers was heavy and supplies of prepared bait nearly ran out, and then on 10th June there was massive feeding at one hopper and the beech under which it nestled had massive stripping along all its root spurs. The bait was replenished and just 24 hours later, on a quick inspection visit, one nearby tree was virtually ring barked and another bared a gaping 10 inch square wound of newly exposed creamy-coloured wood. In the hopper, just yards away, all bait in the tray behind the lip had been consumed overnight. Slight evidence of red staining on the wounded trees showed that the animal doing the damage was also the one hungrily feeding on the bait with its crimson dye. A search of the wood for other damage revealed several trees with fresh patch nibbling. As in 1999 I was dismayed and upset by this renewed assault: my notes record: God is teaching me not to treat the wood as my god. He allows this damage, I must respect this and see that 'moth and rust do not destroy'. This is an allusion to what Jesus teaches in the Sermon on the Mount in Matthew's gospel about our attitude to material things and possessions. Such things, like our delightful wood, will one day pass away and certainly cannot be taken along at the end of one's days, though it can be left for our successors in as good a shape as possible. To think that the wretched grey squirrel should prompt such philosophical thoughts.

The next visit to the wood was a mere two days later when en route to a meeting with Blackwell Science about marketing a two-volume book entitled *The Forests Handbook* of which I was editor. It was with some trepidation. A hasty assay revealed a little fresh stripping and some hitherto unnoticed patch nibbling on beech trees near the new seat. There was nothing more serious as far as could be seen and I drove on to the planned rendezvous at the Newbury Hilton Hotel rather more at ease. My notes for the day inserted PTL—Christian shorthand for 'praise the Lord'.

Three days later, on 16th June, this time en route to Oxford, a brief stop was again made to check for fresh damage. It was early, and a glorious mid-summer's morning. The sun shafted through the trees illuminating greens, olives and lovats of every verdant hue. But as brilliant, penetrating and surgically precise as the sunlight was, it revealed no new damage. There was one spot of patch nibbling previously missed; however, the dull brownish colour of the exposed wood, like a bruised or cut-open apple, showed it was several days old. There was no more damage that month, or in July.

Had the whole early June skirmish been with one belligerent squirrel which, to varying degrees, tested and stripped 15 or 20 beeches mainly in the vicinity of the hopper it had taken a liking to? Feeding at this hopper ceased at the same time as new stripping stopped. Hoppers were gathered up and emptied on 2nd August.

The year 2001 held mixed prospects. The beech would no longer be responding so vigorously to the thinning now four years ago and they are getting older and gradually growing beyond the most vulnerable age. By contrast 2000 was a very heavy mast year, that is, all over southern England, including in our woodland, beech trees set masses of seed and branches were laden with their nut-like fruits. The autumn saw the ground strewn with them, tough, leathery and reddish brown, persisting all through winter. This profusion only happens every eight or ten years and is an inexhaustible food supply for grey squirrels. In times past, when such mast occurred swine were turned into a wood—pannage—both to feed off the beech's largesse and also trample the nuts into the soil so beginning the process of regeneration. The year 2001 was not bad for damage. Some appeared in early July and perhaps a dozen trees bore scars of patch nibbling or a few rather larger strippings, but the notes are mild in tone. Each year a little more is learned, but at times I think not only by me!

I had not intended writing a whole chapter on squirrels. They do occupy more time than any other single task caring for the wood, so perhaps it's understandable. While I don't entirely share the Duke of Edinburgh's sentiment quoted on Radio 4's evening news on 5th June 2000 that 'introduction of grey squirrels has done far more damage to the environment than GM crops ever would', they are undoubtedly the single greatest scourge assaulting the growth of broadleaved woodlands in the lowlands of Britain. Many foresters have abandoned attempts to grow quality hardwoods for this reason. Unbelievably, the one poison that can be used to kill grey squirrels is about to be withdrawn since warfarin has long been superseded by more potent, second generation, rodenticides. Indeed, we live in the super-rat triangle of Berkshire, Hampshire and Surrey where rats are resistant to conventional warfarin poison. Thus with widespread use of other pesticides to control such vermin there was little point in permitting continued use of an outdated chemical and with remarkable alacrity in 1999 Europe, or rather Brussels, was on the verge of banning warfarin as a matter of good housekeeping. No one, it seems, remembered that its one continuing use, in a special formulation much different from that now becoming ineffective against rats, remained central in the war against grey squirrels. With only days to go British representatives woke up to the fact (after all we couldn't expect other European countries to be concerned) that grey squirrels are a peculiarly British problem. There is none anywhere else in Europe apart from a small population in the Po valley in northern Italy. Fortunately for the great beech and oak forests of France and Germany, it was only the English who from late Victorian times began importing this exotic arboreal creature from the north-east states of America. Doubtless the introductions were made to entertain and amuse owners of private estates, but it is the squirrel that has had the last laugh.

The grey squirrel has adapted so well to our country that it is equally at home in a woodland or a domestic garden. Their cavorting on and conquering of the bird table are rapidly passing into folklore. Our own efforts have been thwarted by a squirrel that hangs by the tips of it hind paws to stretch the length of the bird food dispenser to get at every last nut, seed and grain of wheat. And our nights in autumn 2001 were disturbed by rustling and rummaging as at least one grey squirrel, probably the one attracted to the bird table, began building a drey in the loft right above our bedroom. It arrived each evening and would leave early in the morning, but we don't know where it got in, and to get rid of it was enormous trouble. But for all that they do entertain and their posture is positively endearing. All will recognize Humbert Wolfe's perfect opening description, to which my mother, knowing my antipathy for the animal, drew my attention, and which every forester, while agreeing with action taken, will puzzle over the closing lines!

The grey squirrel

Like a small grey
coffee pot,
sits the squirrel.
He is not
all he should be,
kills by dozens
trees, and eats
his red-brown cousins.

The keeper on the
other hand,
who shot him, is
a Christian, and
loves his enemies
which shows
the squirrel was not
one of those.

Humbert Wolfe, 1924

(reproduced by permission, © Ann Wolfe)

It seems likely that use of warfarin, this most efficient means of control, will be denied the grower of broadleaved trees within a year or two. Forest Research are still working towards an effective contraceptive which will curtail population numbers and some progress has been made in predicting when serious squirrel damage is likely to occur. For the time being the immediate outlook is bleak. For the wood live trapping seems the only option, and fortunately we only have one small area to contend with. It is fortunate too that most of the trees are getting beyond the really vulnerable age. However, cleaning in Taid's Wood in early 2002 revealed many of the 15-year-old stems of sycamore coppice to be badly gnawed near the top where they were about an inch or two thick. The squirrel wars, it seems, are not yet over.

Grey squirrel damage is a scourge of broadleaved woodlands and has no redeeming features. Not everything in a wood that appears to harm is like that. There is a fungus that decays oak heartwood, but so slowly and in such a way that it can add hundreds of pounds to the value of a single oak log. It is rare, but one such 'brown oak' turned up in Nain's Copse in 1994. The merchants took most of it, but a little was left, and it went a long way.

*Hazelnut shells
left by grey
squirrels*

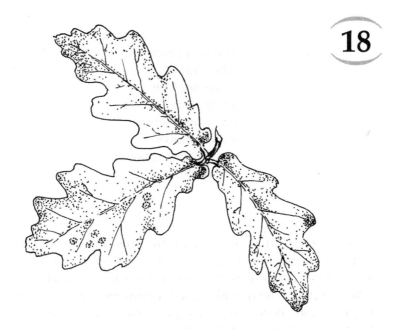

18

What happened to the brown oak

When the oak standards were thinned in 1994, in the newly acquired and very dense adjoining wood that we named Nain's Copse, one of the 43 mature trees turned out to be a 'brown' oak. This is an oak that has become infected by the beefsteak fungus, *Fistulina hepatica* to give it its scientific name, which provokes the tree into an unusual response. Long before incipient decay develops, the heartwood turns a rich nutty brown. This reaction is extensive and all the wood inside the lower bole can be transformed from the ordinary, and pleasant, pale and mellow oak to a remarkable and stunningly attractive deep brown, dark enough to match an antique oak table or dresser. And here lies its great value. This naturally stained wood can be readily used to effect repairs on such precious furniture and consequently the rare log of brown oak commands premium prices. Nothing external to the tree reveals what value it contains; it turned up as a bonus for us in the thinning.

The brown oak was sufficiently important to be highlighted in the sale particulars as a feature of the parcel of otherwise average oak logs. When the fellers cut the 'brown oak' it was found to be about 155 years old, whereas most of the oaks thinned out across the four acres of Nain's Copse were closer to 115 years of age. It was in a line of mature trees along the northern edge of Nain's copse next to Mr Thirlstrup's field, the farmer who works the land to the north of the wood, and was the only one to be cut. Most were either overmature and full of holes or so heavily branched low down as to have only a short bole. They were and still are far too majestic and striking to fell and far more valuable left for wildlife. For decades, if not for a century or more, they will provide a home for numerous birds in which to nest, to roost, and to feed and for countless beetles and other insects to do whatever they do. Nevertheless, one old timer was felled, and is now rendering service that, in its way, is just as precious.

Once on the ground, the brown oak was 'dressed' like all the other oaks being offered for sale. This means that its branches were cut off, and the log cut through at a point at or near crown break to afford the longest possible length. Both the felling and the subsequent dressing are highly skilled. If it is poorly done, the potential of a fine oak can be ruined. In *A Wood of Our Own* it was likened to a diamond cutter who can make or break the transformation from uncut rough diamond to a gemstone of great beauty. For the brown oak one particular facet needed establishing. How far up the bole did the rich brown staining extend? We knew it was at the base where the tree was sawn through, but did it reach 10 feet, 20 feet or even higher? The fellers first sliced off the bottom one foot or so because here in the centre some decay had begun although most of the cross-section was still sound. Above this large hunk two cuts were made, one at about eight feet and another at twice this height. Although it wasn't possible to roll the logs apart to inspect the cross-sections, the nutty brown sawdust at eight feet showed plenty of staining present, but at 16 feet there was considerably less. These cuts would help buyers inspecting the brown oak to value it. Indeed, large logs of all the valuable hardwoods like oak, ash, beech, sycamore, sweet chestnut and wild cherry are always felled first and sold at stump, i.e. where they fall, or at rideside. This allows both buyer and seller to judge the quality of the parcel, to see how much decay there is, to look for harmful cracks known as shakes, and to note staining whether desirable such as our brown oak or olive ash, or as a defect such as blackheart in ash and red heart in beech. After our oak parcel was bought all the logs, including those of the brown oak, were dragged by tractor to the entrance and thence from there to the sawmill. That is the last time they were seen. All that was left behind on the floor of the now more open woodland of Nain's Copse was the cordwood cut from the branches, the branch piles themselves fanning out where each tree had fallen, and the precision-cut stump surfaces attended by neat piles of sawdust, wedges of wood like cut cheese, and other offcuts testifying to the skill of the fellers. And there was the foot-thick hunk from the brown oak languishing perched on its parent stump.

At its core, decay in this bottom section of the brown oak was not so advanced as to make it hollow and so create something like a huge dirty polo mint six feet across. But, no further thought was given to it. Nettles grew up around the old stump with its Easter Island-like topknot, a hopeful oak coppice shoot sprouted vigorously and so far has evaded the attentions of roe deer, and the topknot-like hunk itself was alternately soaked and dried, frozen and warmed as season followed season. Occasionally it cropped up in conversation, mainly regarding whether it was worth cutting and gleaning the few remains of the brown oak for ourselves. Certainly only the innermost core was decayed, the outer brown parts of the cross-section appeared quite sound. Mostly, it lay forgotten.

About a year after the oaks were thinned the cordwood was finally sold to some friends from the church where we once

worshipped, the Wyeths. They owned a farm a few miles from where we live and cut and sold firewood in the winter to provide some extra income. By the time they bought the cordwood it was well seasoned. But they had a difficult time because November 1995 was a very wet month and both the main ride and the one running along the bottom next to the railway line became very muddy as the firewood was extracted. It was arduous work, as indeed is the whole firewood business to the point that, a year later, when enquiring of Gordon Wyeth's possible interest in thinning the beech, he reported that the family had chucked in this side of their business as a bit of a loss. Perhaps struggling manfully and muddily with 20 odd cords one wet November proved the last straw.

On most visits there was no reason to pass the brown oak hunk. It was at the farthest part of the wood, and in summer was shrouded by nettles, although the open day route did go right passed it. Margaret and I would occasionally remark that it might be worth seeing if anything could be made from it. The first time a piece was cut out to experiment with was in 1997, after it had been exposed to the elements for three years. Two square blocks, with sides equal to the length of the chainsaw's drawbar reach of 12 inches, were cut away. They proved astonishingly heavy and clearly still wet, and had to be hauled up to the entrance in the shiny new wheelbarrow. These two cubical lumps of wood then languished in the boot of the car for weeks until eventually taken to a 'dealer' in unusual woods and timbers who supplied blanks and flats for the large wood turning business. His mill and wood store were in Alresford, about 10 miles from where we live, and with some excitement, the two rough lumps of brown oak were offered for sale. No deal was struck, he already had plenty in stock and could buy logs or much larger pieces than I was clutching whenever he needed them. His 'shop', piled to the ceiling on every side with all sorts of exotic woods, revealed the extent of interest in woodturning. Unbelievably, wood turners have three magazines dedicated exclusively to their hobby! However, the two brown oak blanks were unsold and unused, not to mention the much larger hunk still lying uncared for in the wood.

The next foray was to advertise them in *Woodlots*, the trade magazine that so successfully helped market the thinning of the beech. Advertising is free, and there was one enquiry. This was from a wood turner living just round the corner! In April 1998 he called to see the sorry looking pieces laid out on the garage floor. His interest was sufficient to ask about the price. At this point my status as novice with anything to do with woodturning imploded in on me and I muttered 'a fiver'. And that is what I got for the pair. But this transaction did confirm that the brown oak had turning potential and it encouraged me to labour on steadily to cut more blanks from the hunk that still rested topknot style on the old stump in the far corner of Nain's Copse. The rich brown sawdust that attended the tiring efforts to cut out each time the largest possible piece with the chainsaw will remain fresh in the memory. What remains fresh in my youngest son, Ben's, memory are the two occasions he helped. The whole hunk couldn't be cut up in one go, there was far too much, and it took four visits spread over twice as many months to complete the task. What Ben remembers is hauling 3 or 4 chunks of it all the way up to the entrance in the wheelbarrow, pulling it as if harnessed like a packhorse, his shoulder-length hair at the time the equal of any mane. His dad was grateful, only having to carry the saw. The first few pieces were stored in the garage to season and it was indirectly because of Margaret's heart attack in July 1998—from which she fully recovered—that these hitherto unpromising brown oak blanks came into their own.

The purchaser who bought the first pieces for a fiver unexpectedly came back on to the scene three-and-half years later. In an internet search about woodturning, a website for Laymar Crafts featured book reviews, and one of them was of *A Wood of Our Own* even though it has only a little in it about woodturning. And this is what it says. 'I was introduced, no conned into buying this book when Julian advertised for sale some small pieces of Brown Oak from an old stump in the Wood. I turned up to make an offer for a couple of pieces which he accepted, then preceded to sell me his book.' The reviewer then remarks that such a book probably wouldn't appeal, and goes on: 'The fact that I had some wood from the Wood and that the actual tree (well stump) is mentioned and shown in one of the illustrations was perhaps a better reason to read what turned out to be a little gem of a book and any thought of being conned soon evaporated.' The website even features a scanned picture of the book's cover. The 'I' in the review is the proprietor of Laymar Crafts, Richard Stapley. He never told me about the review.

In Alton where we live there is a pioneering heart rehabilitation programme which was the inspiration and initiative of Dr Hugh Bethell. He was appointed MBE for his Rehab work, as it is called. A key part of Rehab is systematic exercising in controlled ways suited to each patient's condition. After coming out of hospital Margaret began this course and has continued ever since. You begin slowly, but surprisingly quickly build up a reasonable level of fitness so crucial to helping the heart stay healthy. It was during these sessions that Margaret met Pete, who was similarly recovering from a heart condition. They got talking and Margaret learned of Pete's passion for wood turning that he had been pursuing for some five years, and he learned of our wood—incidentally located on the other side of Basingstoke from where he lived. And that was enough. A session or two later Margaret gave Pete one of the brown oaks chunks. He turned it into an elegant bowl. Later Pete and his wife, Beth, came for coffee and we told them more about our wood and he showed us his handiwork including his speciality of delicate almost paper thin wooden tulips. And then came one of life's rich coincidences. Beth, it turned out, had lived at Ivy Cottage, Steventon, as a teenager when her father worked as a gardener on the Steventon estate in the early 1950s at just the time the owners, the Hutton-Crofts, sold Northdown Plantation to the Forestry Commission. Her main recollection of the owners was the kindness of Mrs Hutton-Croft who always took tea with her workers and passed on old darned skirts. Pete kindly took some more of our rough brown oak blanks along with a copy of *A Wood of Our Own* as a thank you. I hope he didn't feel conned! Indeed, he enjoyed working with this unusual oak, and what he fashioned displayed the richness of grain and depth of colour and with clearly an eye for style. We were glad to meet Pete and Beth, even if the original reason of a heart attack was obviously not by choice. God works in His own ways. As William Cowper, the great 18th Century hymnist, penned: 'Behind a frowning providence, He hides a smiling face.'

Pete turned four bowls and crafted a small shelf, a quadrant, to fit a corner of our living room. We kept one bowl; the others have been gifts. The first went to my mother, Nain to our boys, as a birthday present: this was fitting, the fine brown oak came from Nain's Copse. My mother-in-law was also given one to mark the special occasion of her 88th birthday. The third and largest bowl Pete turned resides in one of the great stately homes of Britain.

For 20 years His Grace the Duke of Buccleuch and Queensberry was president of the Commonwealth Forestry Association. His retirement from office in May 1999 was marked by the Association's visit to Boughton House and to the woodlands on his Northamptonshire estate. The occasion was commemorated in two ways: a traditional tree planting ceremony as one would expect and a presentation of Pete's finest bowl. The traditional tree planting was as special as Pete's bowl since a 'royal' oak tree was planted. It was one raised from acorns gathered in Windsor Great Park from beneath the oaks planted for each country of the Commonwealth to mark Her Majesty's accession to the throne in 1952 and coronation in 1953. The acorn mast had been prolific in 1996 and many had been gathered especially from beneath the oak planted for Zimbabwe, or Southern Rhodesia as it had been. It was fitting that the Association's regional chairman from Zimbabwe was present at Boughton and helped the Duke to plant the young oak. But for us it was brown oak bowl, with an engraved silver plaque, that was even more special, coming as it did from a tree that had stood in our wood. As the Association's vice-chairman I had the honour of presenting it to His Grace and expressing gratitude for his services to us for more than two decades.

One of the Association's members present at the Boughton House meeting was Dr John Brazier who had been Britain's foremost wood scientist. Just prior to the presentation he examined the bowl intently, slowly turning it round in his experienced hands, and finally pronounced it as genuine brown oak! Foresters are notoriously poor at identifying timbers from the trees they so carefully grow, and knowing what was claimed for the bowl—true brown oak—was authentic was welcome. What is not known is in which of His Grace's three stately homes the bowl now resides.

Our stay at Boughton House was one of those rare and wholly unexpected occasions. Margaret and I, along with other office bearers of the Commonwealth Forestry Association, were invited to stay at the house rather than have to find our own accommodation. We assumed we would be allocated a room in some annex, but when we arrived the annex turned out to be a royal bedchamber originally prepared for a visit by King William of Orange in about 1700. He never in fact used it and only dined at Boughton. We did use the bedroom and spent a night surrounded by priceless tapestries draping every wall and fine antique furniture not even in need of repair from a bit of brown oak! We hadn't realised our invitation was as guests of the Duke and Duchess themselves.

A more gracious 24 hours was hard to imagine as our every wish was attended to in this great country house in Northamptonshire known as the Versailles of England.

Pete also fashioned a small shelf from the brown oak. It was the idea of erecting a shelf that had spurred our interest to do something with the topknot of oak in the first place. My mother had passed to us a striking piece of Minton parian ware, a figurine of Miranda, dating from 1851. As a child she had seen this 15 inch high statue with its white marble-like lustre, and thought it exquisite beyond compare. It had resided in my parents' home for all the years I can remember, and now we were its custodians but we really had no safe place to display it. Then the thought: why not on its own corner shelf to complement our Victorian oak bureau and bookshelf? And the perfect choice of wood for such a purpose was the already aged brown oak. Thanks to Pete it has become reality and Miranda sits safely and is fixed securely on her own very special shelf.

The fine oak tree, the felling of which yielded so much of interest, was one in a line of old oaks along the northern boundary of Nain's Copse. Its removal left a gap, not an obvious one perhaps, but a discontinuity nevertheless. We filled it in May 1996 by planting another oak about eight feet from where the brown oak had been. This was a special planting and became only the second tree in the wood to have its own commemorative plaque, in this instance 'Nain's oak, planted on the occasion of her 85th birthday, May 1996'. All the family gathered for the ceremony and Nain duly added a spadeful or two of soil. May is rather late to be planting trees though it was a help that the spring that year was cold. Even so, with Nain's oak a five foot high feathered whip, regular bucketfuls of water soaked the soil in the succeeding weeks to help it become established. Since then it has survived the attentions of rabbits and deer and, after a shaky couple of years when it looked decidedly 'peaky', it is now growing reasonably vigorously and was particularly helped by the wet and run of exceptional growing seasons since 1998. It is in a fertile spot if the luxuriance of nettle growth is an indication. Whether by being planted so close to the old brown oak stump it too will pick up the beefsteak fungus and develop the rare exotic colouring, only Nain's great, great, great, great grandchildren will discover if the wood, of course, is still in the family.

Only one chunk of brown oak remains in the garage. It certainly won't be thrown out now that the value and great beauty of this wood has been revealed. All the other rough chainsaw hewn pieces have been turned into goblets each of a size dictated by the available dimensions to work with. It remains a marvel that they came from the great partly-decayed hunk that survived four years neglect atop the old stump, but it is good we finally discovered its true worth.

It was also good to discover the popularity of wood turning. Not only have I given a talk about the wood to the Hampshire Woodturners Association, when 80 or so enthusiasts turned out on a warm July evening only to be cooped up to watch slides, but several have visited the wood following a tempting offer. Some months after the talk I suggested to the chairman that if members of his association were interested they could come to the wood and, within reason, choose to have felled for £20 any tree that they thought would have some wood turning potential. On two Saturday mornings in January and February 2000 a handful turned up in response to the offer. They toured the wood to look at trees that I had mentally selected in advance as being of probable interest. Not only did my choices elicit no interest, but what was chosen was quite unexpected.

The first candidate for felling was a dead beech about 8 inches across. It had been dead for at least a year and, as with all beech, there was always a chance the wood might feature the fine black lines from incipient fungal decay known as spalting. These lines, black as Indian ink, meander through the wood and are most striking when turned. Like the brown oak, fungal ingress enhances rather than devalues the wood. And spalted the dead beech proved to be. No sooner had the chainsaw finished its work and slowed to tick over, my woodturning visitors, like vultures to the kill, gathered round the cut end of the now prostrate tree voicing connoisseurs' grunts and asking for lengths to be cut off. Several were. The next tree was a large uprooted birch left propped up on a nearby hazel; it had been like this since a storm some three years before, reclining at a steep angle with few roots still in soil contact. It had been dead for at least two years. Careful sawing through, in case there was still tension in the trunk awaiting release, revealed the usual incipient decay of birch's soft and non-durable wood. But that is not what the visitors saw. For them there was patterning of beiges and pale yellows, off-whites and creams, blotched across the surface like an irregular, much faded chessboard.

Several lengths were cut off and retrieved as trophies. The next tree was certain to be of interest, the long fallen yew in Nain's copse which we call Jane Austen's yew because we surmise with reason she will have seen it on many of the countryside outings she so loved when growing up in Steventon. The literary link may have been lost on our visitors, but not the fine rich reddish-brown of yew wood that contrasts so vividly with the milky white of its sapwood. In all, the trees felled were, in forestry terms, of no value. Being paid, and willingly so, £20 for each of them merely confirmed the proverb that 'one man's muck is another man's brass'.

The fallen yew, Jane Austen's yew, has also provided a gift. Pete, who had turned most of the brown oak, did the same with a large square block of yew to craft a bowl for my mother's 90th birthday. It was difficult to find a large piece free from rot and several were excised from the prostrate yew tree with the chainsaw only to be discarded. One block finally made the grade, but even though the tree had been dead for 13 years, and presumably was well seasoned, when Pete got it, it was soaking. Its sodden, waterlogged condition made turning a delight and the lathe's sharp knives quickly yielded a rough shape. But it was very wet and Beth, his wife, first soaked up excess moisture with paper towelling and then micro-waved it. The bowl did have a few defects but Pete skilfully turned these to advantage by burning out cracks, charring them black. It is a choice bowl embellished with a silver plaque engraved with mother's details.

One of the Hampshire woodturners who came was the

Jane Austen's yew, inspected by John White, at stop 9

Association's chairman, David Foot. He came a second time on his own wanting a large limb or stem of ash. On the edge of Nain's Copse, overlooking a wildlife glade, there was an ash tree with a large limb possibly of coppice origin or from a very low fork that was both straight and of sufficient thickness that David might consider suitable. He did, and it was carefully felled and then cut into four-foot lengths. After tidying up the branchwood other work beckoned and David was left to his own devices. He set about cleaving each of the four-foot lengths using both steel and wooden wedges. Ash splits quite readily and each log was 'quartered' into five or six pieces. He wanted them for chair legs and because splitting follows the grain the legs would have the best possible strength. With another £20 pocketed both owner and turner were well satisfied. Two years later David came again and repeated the cleaving process using lengths cut from a dangerously leaning and much older ash tree that his visit provided the excuse finally to cut down. This older ash was in payment for David turning for us four exquisite brown oak goblets from the last but one piece of brown oak.

That is what happened to the brown oak.

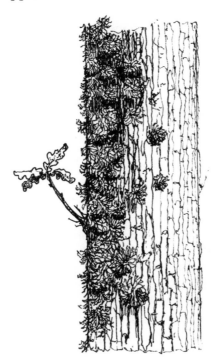

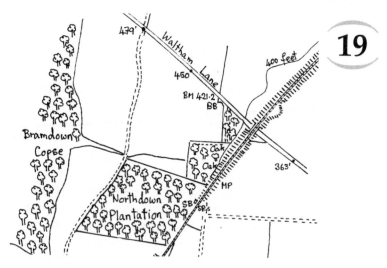

19

'All I want is a wood somewhere'

Following our first open day Duff Hart-Davis, *The Independent's* countryside and rural affairs feature writer, crafted a flattering piece. He entitled it as I have this chapter, and told of the delights of his visit to the wood and shared his own hankering after some woodland. And such interest is not confined to Britain. Two admirers of *A Wood of Our Own* living in Australia took me to lunch in April 2001. It was an exotic Turkish affair, short only of the seven veils, at the refurbished Vivaldi's restaurant on the Australian National University's Canberra campus. They enthused how even the account of an English wood had chimed with their interests and which they felt many would share in Australia. My generous hosts, in both senses, were Heather Crompton, the president of the Institute of Foresters of Australia, and Dr Suzette Searle renowned expert on Australian acacias. It was only as we began the sweet that the reason for this free lunch emerged—what had happened to the wood in the years since the first book had been published? So both in England and 10,000 miles away there is this desire to care for one's own patch.

Such interest had led to *A Wood of Our Own* selling quite well including a reprinting. Indeed, writing the book about the wood brought experiences and opportunities quite unlooked for as chapter 5, in part, relates. But I found something quite new also. The book made a very personal gift, not only for family and friends at Christmas, but by way of a 'thank-you' or as presentation copies. Such has been its usefulness on many occasions and at many events from Santiago to Sparsholt, from artisans to ambassadors and the aristocracy, and with audiences from National Trust talks to university teaching. It all underscored an interest.

The popularity of owning a corner of England's agreeably sylvan countryside means that small woodlands rarely come on to the open market. Although agents such as John Clegg and Sons, Savills, and English Woodlands, to name but three, maintain lists of woodlands for sale, and there is even a website of this name 'Woodlands for Sale' run by the Hantons, most of the time transactions are completed as seller finds buyer through local knowledge and enquiry. Indeed, in Hampshire, in the late 1990s a friend has been searching for suitable woodland for three years, and of three inspected all have sold well above the asking price. One of the questions arising from *A Wood of Our Own* is about what to look for when buying a wood, not so much in a silvicultural sense of what the trees are like, but as a property subject to an array of possible conditions and constraints. Like buying a house, what should one look out for and ask about when considering a wood? Northdown Plantation itself can illustrate several of the points.

The first essential of good access when thinking about buying a wood was mentioned in an earlier chapter, and this aspect helped make up our minds. John White's pen and ink sketch map of the wood on the book's frontispiece shows this as well as any ordnance survey map. A lane, a public highway, runs the length of our western boundary. From it a wide bell mouth entrance opens on to a track with turning area. This track is metalled for the first 30 yards or so, just sufficient to support laden timber lorries. The track runs right through the wood and is intercepted halfway by a cross ride. At the bottom 'T' junction spurs lead off to both right and left. Access to and within the wood is excellent. Getting timber to market from the wood and getting equipment to any part of it will never cause insurmountable problems.

The good access is not, as mentioned before, for our exclusive use. The lane, of course, is a public thoroughfare and over the years I have felt bound to clear mud from it when deposited in quantities by timber extraction operations, and to keep the hedges trimmed back at least every second year. This is sometimes helped by a local farmer who takes his combine harvester and straw laden lorries along the lane: we have all seen wisps of hay and straw combed from bails like carding of wool and fall like confetti as they have rubbed too close to hedges, not to mention overhanging branches. Occasionally Sally or Nick Armstrong, who live just beyond the wood, have helpfully phoned to report a fallen branch obstructing the lane. Ownership runs to the lane's dead centre line, and duty of care for one's own boundary. With good access, comes good neighbourliness.

We also share the main track through the wood with Railtrack. This right was granted 40 years ago and it is important to check terms and conditions of such rights, in particular the responsibilities it places on the wood's owner—in our case we must keep the track open at all times, and on the grantee—in Railtrack's case a contribution to maintenance resulting from their exercising this right of access. We share locks on the entrance gates, with Railtrack's and ours at each end of the chain. They are supposed to be left with shanks interlinked, as if arm in arm, so that either party can gain access. It doesn't always happen. Fortunately I have a key for Railtrack's padlock as well as one for ours. But it is important to know who has rights over the proposed purchase.

As well as access rights, the property may be subject to easements like the one we granted Southern Electric for a cable from Mike's smallholding to Railtrack's substation. Easements may curtail use of land and should be listed or included in sale particulars. Covenants may exist too. Northdown Plantation required the lessees, while the property was held as a lease, to maintain the fence along the southern boundary. We were never asked to comply with this obligation since the adjoining field never carried livestock, and is now Mike's Northdown Orchard. Moreover it was extinguished when we acquired the freehold in 1994. However, when at this time we bought Nain's Copse the vendor's solicitors did try to attach restrictions as if the land could one day be used for housing. Most were negotiated away through persistence and persuasion. Clearly these kinds of details emerge in searches and during conveyancing, but all merit careful consideration. One wants to enjoy a woodland and not feel hemmed in.

Care for what the property's deeds require of an owner has today to be extended to the duty of care towards visitors, both invited and uninvited. Public liability is not proscribed by 'Keep out' notices or an absence of rights of way, and all owners need both to take reasonable care to minimise hazards to safety and to

have adequate insurance. Ours is part of a group scheme with the Small Woods Association which they negotiate with the insurers, Bervale Mead, and costs £35 per year for liability cover up to £5 million. At the time of writing the implications of 'Right to roam' await to be worked out in practice, though it seems likely that the smaller owner will be little affected.

One duty placed on landowners is control of vermin and eradication of noxious weeds. For us the principal vermin are rabbits and grey squirrels. The latter tiresomely have still had to have a chapter of their own, chapter 17, but the former are not in the numbers they were when we first acquired Northdown Plantation. However, they haven't been vigorously controlled for a few years and burrows and numbers are slowing increasing. The only noxious weeds are a few ragwort in Taid's wood. We are thankfully free of Japanese knotweed, and the massively invasive rhododendrons that threaten so many woodlands on the acid soils of western Britain, but have to put up with *Clematis*, so at home on our chalky soils, and ever increasing numbers of nettles.

What we are not free from and not blessed by is dumping of

rubbish, especially over or in front of the entrance gates. All landowners suffer this scourge and its nasty cousin 'fly tipping' to a greater or lesser extent, but entrances to woods with recessed gates for convenient parking, remoteness, and which are not over-looked and certainly unlit, invite other people's dirt and detritus. Loo paper, and its emergency substitutes, are discarded at the wood almost daily, condoms most weeks, fridges and other obso-lete white goods every few months, and something exceptional at least once in most years. The most exceptional of recent years occurred the weekend after landfill tax was introduced and some cowboy tree hacker—tree surgeon would be a compliment—drove to the wood to dump the day's trimmings and hackings.

I had spent Saturday morning at the wood and there was nothing untoward about the entrance. Forty-eight hours later, on Monday morning, and en route to Oxford for a Commonwealth Forestry Association meeting, the usual brief visit was made. On the left of the entrance was a neat, compact, cubically shaped pile of branch trimmings. Closer inspection by eye and inescapably by nose showed it to be apple wood with plenty of bruised, decom-posing and fermenting yellow-brown apples, but it was the shape of the debris that gave away its genesis. The trimmings must have been well packed into a pick-up truck and by the time our wood's entrance was selected as the dumping ground, the whole woody and cidery mass had developed a coherence—though no sweet-ness—such that the perpetrators must simply have slid the tangle of branches and twigs off the truck's bed. It kept its shape where it fell, looking like an enormous flattened cube of shrink-wrapped firewood without the plastic. This was not all. Thrown on top of the pile was a cracked water cistern and a piece of old tarpaulin added for good measure. One can imagine the conversation: 'The tree's done and we're off to the landfill with the trimmings'. 'Be a darlin, can you take the broken cistern and tarpaulin as well?' My brief Monday morning visit was that no longer and I went to see Mike. He kindly agreed to pick up the cistern and tarpaulin to be disposed when next rubbish was being collected from Northdown Orchard, and with his tractor fork-lifted the apple trimmings into the wood as 'free' organic matter. Since that dumping, thankfully nothing comparable has occurred.

Two days after writing the above I witnessed with increasing incredulity just how such packing down of branches is achieved. It was a cool sunny Saturday in early May 2001, the first real spring-like weekend after interminable months of cloud and rain, and almost everyone was out in the garden. Our neighbours across the close decided to decapitate their overgrown hedge of Leyland cypress: readers in England will empathise with the need to get on top of this common garden menace. A 'tree services' company had come to do the work. As branches, crown wood and wiry stems emerged from the back garden through the side gate they were piled on the flat bed of the company's 1½ ton pick-up that was parked in their drive. And then it began. One of the two workers, clad in a green boiler suit, clambered on to the branch wood on the back of the truck chainsaw in hand and fired it up. A cloud of blue smoke and engine whine was followed by cutting uncertainly back and forth at the springy pile beneath his feet. Oblivious of danger, but doubtless long practised at such dancing and bouncing on such a woody trampoline, the operator wore no gloves, no goggles, no ear plugs, no hard hat, no toughened thigh guards—just an inscrutable expression. Blue smoke belched, noise rent the May morning. At times so deep did the cutting go that the pile seemed on fire as the saw's oil rich sapphire coloured exhaust fumes escaped upwards. But the disorganised heap of branches was cut down, squashed and made to conform to the truck's shape. The journey to the landfill site, or wherever the debris was destined, would allow further settling and shaping, just as corn-flakes do in the packet that you find is never full when opened! Thus was explained how the tangle of apple branch wood was found so cubic in shape.

This worst incident of fly tipping was discovered within hours of the crime, and so only disfigured the entrance briefly, because of making a quick call at the wood on the way to another destination. This raises two important points when considering purchase of woodland or, indeed, any non-residential property. How far away is it and how convenient is its location? We have found that the 17 miles from where we live is not too far, being a half-an-hour drive and allows a half day's work to be worthwhile without making a visit an expedition in itself. Nearer than say 2 or 3 miles would tempt me to visit far too often, and if farther than, say, 30 miles would make it too far to pop over to or go for a picnic on impulse. Of course, if woodland purchase is just for investment such considerations weigh less heavily, but it is nice to enjoy one's investment in ways beyond the purely monetary!

The question of distance raises too the matter of direction from home. This aspect of location, literally and figuratively, loomed larger than expected in the case of Northdown Plantation and wasn't recognised at the time of purchase. But over the years around three-quarters of all my work-related journeys by car have taken me north-westwards from home. Avoiding Basingstoke (which is always a good thing to do owing to its incompletely developed ring road) when journeying from Alton to Newbury and the M4 or A34, is best effected by going cross-country via Axford in the Candover valley, past Dummer, under the M3 and A303 roads, and along Waltham lane to Overton. This route passes within a few hundred yards of the wood. Both as the Forestry Commission's Chief Research Officer at Alice Holt Lodge near Farnham in the 1990s and more recently as Chairman of the Commonwealth Forestry Association based in Oxford, this journey begins or ends the day's work with its opportunity to call at the wood. With two of my publishers, Oxford University Press and Blackwell Science, also Oxford based, the cache of opportunities for frequent quick visits is overflowing. The downside is occasionally arriving with grubby hands or a bit of dirt in the hair—what's left of it—at the day's committee meeting, lecture or book progress review, from exploring squirrel hopper orifices, picking up entrance litter, or a smearing of oil or rust from the gate locks. It's a small price to pay for the convenience of the wood so often being *en route*.

Uninvited visitors may leave rubbish, but they and many invited visitors often take something away with them if its summertime, and I don't mean picked flowers or scraps of firewood. Unwittingly visitors to the wood will often catch ticks, or rather ticks await a passing animal, and people make perfectly acceptable animals on which to alight. Movement, light coloured clothing or warmth from the skin attracts these tiny creatures which wait for their prey perched on the tip of a blade of grass hoping someone or something will brush past. Once aboard they creep all over the surface looking for a soft fold of skin in which to begin their vampire activities. I often acquire ticks but not everyone seems congenial to the beast. Usually it takes about two days until the mildest of irritations prompts a scratch, and then the discovery of a 'freckle' that wasn't there before. The fact that the 'freckle' can be upended confirms diagnosis of a tick. It can be removed by careful twisting with tweezers but extraction of the head with its embedded mouthparts is important to prevent infection. In 17 years of ownership hundreds of ticks have latched on to me, but none has yet imparted either tick fever or the more feared Lyme's disease.

One becomes used to detecting ticks and used to finding them at strange times and in unexpected places—in both senses of where on the body and where when the discovery is made! The most memorable, if that's the right word, was in Bala, North Wales in May 2000. I was with my mother, my sister, Marilyn, and my niece, Barbara. We were in Bala along with 70 other relatives at a gathering of descendants of Thomas Charles. He is my four greats grandfather, but far more important is that he was one of Wales' great preachers and spiritual leaders of the late eighteenth and earlier nineteenth centuries. He was author of the Welsh Bible Dictionary—*Geriardur Charles*—which, like Matthew Henry's incomparable Bible commentary, is still in use today. Thomas Charles is perhaps best known as the minister to whom the young Mary Jones walked barefoot for 40 miles along paths and rough tracks over the Welsh mountains to buy a bible for which she had been saving up throughout her childhood. Our car journey to Bala could not have been more different from Mary Jones's one on foot, and certainly was not attended by physical discomfort. It was a May day to delight the traveller as my mother and I drove from Hampshire. On the way we called briefly at the wood, to check squirrel hoppers of course, and then for lunch in the hamlet of Dulas near the village of Ewyas Harold about 1½ miles from the Welsh border. We were visiting the Webbs, since Judith runs the Timber Growers Association's woodland initiative with which I help. The intiative aims to assist owners of smaller woodlands, like the Webbs and ourselves, or someone who is thinking of buying one, with the basics of sound forestry and good husbandry. We reached the small town of Bala, nestling on the northern shores of the lake of that name, late in the afternoon of Friday having taken a cross-country route among the green hills, valleys and high moors of mid-Wales.

On the Saturday the much extended family gathered at Plas-yn-dre in the very rooms where Thomas Charles had stayed while courting Sally Jones who, after much entreating, became his wife and thus my four greats grandmother. At dinner, just before the sweet course arrived, I casually explored the tiniest of irritations on my tummy, the kind that a single slight rub usually deals with. A discreet touch was enough to discern a tick. I excused myself, dealt with the problem in the gents. It doubtless hitched its lift to

North Wales early the day before when we stopped briefly to visit the wood.

In Bala, Thomas Charles' reputation is undiminished. Earlier on the day of the dinner, and before the tick disclosed its presence, I visited the Christian bookshop at the southern end of the high street and in conversation with the shop assistant told her about the family gathering. Animatedly and with even a hint of awe, she told the news of the reunion to everyone who came to the shop while I was still there, and perhaps even when I wasn't(!), that descendents of the great man of God were in town. We visited the Calvinistic-Methodist church where he once ministered and stood by his statue that commands the church's entrance for the requisite photographs.

Not all woods have ticks or other threats to beware of when buying one. We enjoy our 30 acres and have added little to it apart from introducing a few native flowers, excavating a pond, and pursuing good forestry to grow fine timber trees, and encourage wildlife. We want to pass it on in as good a shape as possible. The water tank has long gone but in its place metaphorically is now

something much more useful, particularly for my mother and my own ageing and sometimes aching limbs. A seat is now installed by the ride that leads to the pond. It is wooden, of course, and seats two people easily and is the most comfortable of garden seats. It came from our local DIY store, Phillips in Alton, or more correctly from Malaysia and from, I hope, sustainably managed forest. The wood has no shed, which would only invite thieves to break in, even though our helpful neighbour Mike keeps an eye on things generally.

'All I want is a wood somewhere' is surely echoed by many. Such a property, a 'My fair wood' to parody the title's inspiration, is not a burden, can stand neglect, and can be a source of immense pleasure. What these pages have shared may have either encouraged you to do likewise or at least allowed you to share the enjoyment we have had as if our wood, and all that has happened to it, had been your own.

Cone of Douglas fir

Orange tip

Stewards of the wood

This is my second book about the wood we bought in 1985. Owning it has brought much joy and interest of which sharing it in these pages has been a part. It is, too, my hobby. But has it become my god?

I worry about this question in the sense that a 'god' is someone or something we worship, and worship is shown by devotion. It is measured today very largely in the time we give whether supporting Manchester United, playing golf, or genuinely worshipping the living God on the Lord's day. Of course, the wood isn't worshipped in a pagan sense of spirit or tree worship: I worship the Creator not the created, but it seems right to ask the question does the time devoted to it that gives such pleasure begin to usurp the real God and become something of an idol? It is not a fetish in possessing magical powers, it doesn't take over my life in any all-consuming way, but I do devote time to its care and its interests, or rather my interests in it. If it is not a god, it has the risk of becoming one in the sense of being that to which most attention is given.

These are personal reflections—and this short chapter is something of an epilogue. I feel a strong sense of stewardship towards the wood, both the desire to pass on one corner of England's countryside in as best a shape as possible and to share it as far as is practicable. And an unusual visit to the wood in 1999 has helped me reflect on the original question of how devoted I am to it.

Many share a sense of caring for natural things, and not only in England of course. This was amply demonstrated by a visit of two Papua New Guineans in September 1999, Ru and Puklum, who are nationals of the island country atop of Australia and known the world over as PNG. They were in Britain as guests of my sister, Professor Dame Marilyn Strathern, the Mistress of Girton College, Cambridge. As an anthropologist she had met Ru in the early 1960s and Puklum, also known as John Kenny, a few years later and had worked with them, on and off, for more than 30 years. This was their first time to Britain. Indeed, apart from one visit by Ru to Australia, they had never before left PNG. Within PNG itself neither would often leave their home village other than for the nearby town of Mount Hagen some 6000 feet up in the central Highlands. But here they were in Britain and here they were with my sister in the wood. It was their attitude to being in woodland that was revealing, revealing of a relationship—of a kind of stewardship—with the world they inhabited.

As we walked around several things happened. Marilyn translated for us between pidgin English and the kind I speak—it has been more than 20 years since I also worked in PNG and my once rudimentary pidgin is now non-existent. We followed the usual open day trail but made a detour to visit Taid's plaque, the plaque that commemorates my father's life of 80 years and where my mother spread his ashes. Moments before reaching it we glimpsed an inquisitive roe deer that momentarily held us in its gaze before darting for cover among the trees of Taid's Wood. Puklum and Ru pointed and gesticulated, excited at such a sign, which in PNG was considered a favourable omen. Our next stop was by the railway track to enjoy the picnic Margaret had put together for us. While fascinated by the trains that clattered by no more than three or four yards from where we sat, it was the fate of my empty Pepsi Max can that astonished the visitors. The can was too big to fit inside the lunch box, the plastic lid wouldn't close, and I didn't want to carry it or stuff it in a pocket and risk sticky brown stains from the odd drip. I decided, too, against crushing and deforming the cobalt blue receptacle as if defeated in robot wars. Instead, the Pepsi can was wedged into the fork of a nearby hawthorn bush, with the intention of fetching it later. The symbolism of this act to Ru and Puklum was quite lost on me. Animated like youngsters, a torrent poured forth, quite unintelligible to me, and with much waving of arms they pointed to what I had just done. This is the gist of what Marilyn translated from their exclamations in pidgin.

In parts of PNG, after a really satisfying meal, and that is a meal that always includes their staple protein of pork, the pig's lower jawbones are hooked over branches of trees and bushes to acknowledge and placate the spirits of their ancestors. Is this, they wondered, what was being done with the Pepsi can, after all we weren't far from Taid's plaque where my ancestor's ashes, namely my father's, were spread? Moreover, in PNG it is common for the bones to be kept sometimes for generations as a kind of aide-memoire, a bit like a photographic album, with people able to recount the happy time or recall the special occasion of the feast.

The pig's tusks are similarly precious and retained, and added to a necklace as a record of history. All this led to talking about pigs more generally and how in times past in England they would be turned into woodland to forage for acorns or beech mast—exercising the right of pannage—both to feed them and to help cultivate the soil and bury these seeds of oak and beech trees as their snouts snuffled and their trotters trampled. Often the resulting natural regeneration of seedlings was profuse. Of course the Pepsi can is not going to be kept for generations, nor worn round the neck, but it does remain wedged in a cleft of the hawthorn to remind of this brief contact between cultures.

Leaving the wedged Pepsi can and all its evocations, we walked on to visit Nain's oak at the northern end of the wood. While there we saw more roe deer picking their way across a freshly cut field of maize, doubtless including the one we had disturbed earlier. From Nain's oak we began to make our way back to the entrance still following the open day trail. Twice we had to hurry for shelter under beech trees as heavy showers caught us unawares. Though brief, the rain fell in torrents, vertically without a breath of wind, and the humidity was suddenly saturating, the air close and claustrophobic. Such near-tropical downpours comforted our New Guinea visitors and, at last, in this strange unfamiliar scenery and equally unfamiliar culture of England, they felt at home. Indeed, that September was unusually warm and wet and the countryside long remained lush and green. It was recorded as the warmest for 50 years, some 2°C above average. Ru and Puklum felt at home, and said so.

The wedged Pepsi can remained for two years as bright blue as on the day Ru and Puklum visited. Then one day, almost exactly on the second anniversary of their visit, it disappeared. Only two days before, Marilyn had come for tea in our home, after visiting mother in hospital, and for the first time since the Pepsi can incident she and I had talked about it because this final chapter was being drafted. She remembered everything as clearly as I did. Then a few hours later, or was it perhaps even as we had been speaking, 17 miles away and deep in rural Hampshire the can mysteriously vanished from its cleft. Perhaps Ru and Puklum were right, or perhaps my neighbour Mike's kids helped themselves for a bit of fun. Nearby the paraphernalia for open day stop 4 was also freshly disturbed. The can later turned up, lying on the ground part covered in leaves only yards from the hawthorn. Its mild steel skin was already rusting. Next to it, but not as hidden, a violet coloured tropical Tango can had appeared—it does, after all, take two!

So what does the story mean for Christian stewardship? It helped me realise that I share with Ru and Puklum respect for the created order, but attribute it to the One God, not ancestral spirits; I share with them delight in life in all its abundance and vivacity— the roe deer—but not in the sense of an augury of good or evil; and I share with them in appreciating the symbolism trees and shrubs and actions can represent, not as a spiritual power they possess, but in a metaphorical sense of a picture, such as in Psalm 1 the flourishing tree planted by a stream in the desert to which the man trusting in God is likened. Stewardship means being utterly appreciative, caring and enjoying what we are responsible for, but not paying homage or reverence.

Other visitors have been many, and while not leading to spiritual reflection have reflected sometimes the age in which we live. And as related in *A Wood of Our Own*, some have arrived not by road, nor by walking, nor even by rail—the sidings have long gone—but by air. Four more balloons have landed choosing Northdown Plantation for the ignominy and finality of journey's end where gravity finally got the better of lift. They were launched in celebration or in competitions and labelled to tell the world of their business. Unlike the first one, none of the more recent aerial visitors was launched at school fetes. One celebrated a birthday, one the new year of 1997, and two were released skywards at charity fund-raising events. The birthday balloon and the charities reflect our times. In September 1996 I found scraps of yellow balloon that had been launched five days before in Witney near Oxford, a distance of about 40 miles to the northwest. It was an appeal by Usborne CLIC—the cancer leukaemia in children charity. There wasn't enough left of the reply card to send off. The new year balloon turned up in March of the year in question when on a visit with my mother, and was an aluminium foil affair that simply proclaimed 'Happy 1997'. The birthday balloon was also made of foil with a pink Barbie doll print and a curl of damp blue ribbon. It got tangled in the trees of Taid's Wood in January 2000, so perhaps it was a millennium balloon rather than a birthday one, but there was no label to say. A year later the fourth balloon, appropriately forest green in colour and publicizing a charity, had only travelled about 15 miles drifting on a northwest wind from Newbury. It was snagged on some hazel in Nain's Copse and

when found, in March 2001, was 10 days after the closing date for sending in the reply card of distance travelled for the prize of a hot-air balloon flight. It was one of 350 launched on 29th January in aid of 'Nightstop' that helps homeless teenagers and young twenties with a bed for the night to provide 'a breathing space for vulnerable young people to consider the options'. How the balloons encapsulate our times!

We celebrated the millennium, two months before the real start of the third millennium since Christ, in November 2000 with the help of the L plates youth group, our church's young people in the 11–13 year category. Their contribution was to create a time capsule that they buried on a raw Saturday morning. They chose a place near the seat and Paul, Sue, Kirsty, Hannah and Elizabeth did all the dirty work of digging, hacking at roots, and excavating chalk rubble to a depth of two feet. My job was to survey with great care the capsule's position both from the uncertain features of four large trees and by dead reckoning from the intersection where the main track and cross rides meet. These survey data only need to be good enough to help us find the capsule, a tough plastic ice cream carton enclosing its precious polythene-wrapped contents, in 10 years time when the current L Plates felt it ought to be dug up. In that time probably two thinnings of the beech will test the care with which we buried the treasure: tree felling and log extraction mess up soil gouging ruts and compacting soft ground. The wood, too, will look different. The beech will be taller and standing beneath them feel ever more cathedral-like, though long years will still remain before final felling and starting over again.

In eight years time, when the capsule is dug up, it would be just when another instalment of the wood's story is perhaps ready for writing, though I cannot conceive that as much will happen as it has in the last eight. The future is in God's hands, we are but stewards of the wood, my words and this story will pass away, the only certain thing is that the words in the time capsule will not. Double wrapped inside the L Plates' plastic container are passages of the Bible: they are Christ's words which, as He said, 'Heaven and earth will pass away but...but my words will never pass away'. Such is the gospel.

The time I give to managing the wood, averaging two half-a-days a month, is not in danger of making it an obsession. It has not become a 'god', but reflecting on the question has not been unhealthy. It reminds, too, that nothing should usurp the One who should take first place.

We have owned the wood for 17 years. It's a living organism and what happened to it has been told. It is a community of trees that is not, in one sense, finite in time while the Earth remains, but is always changing, regenerating, growing or suffering storms. Our role is to guide its development to fulfil our responsibility to grow fine timber for future generations to enjoy, and be somewhere enjoyed by wildlife and by people who visit. That is what I believe is meant by stewardship of creation which is the first instruction God gave us—to look after wisely and caringly what He has made, while at the same time using our labour to benefit from its fruitfulness. As for trees themselves, they have a special place in the heart of the Almighty. Of nothing else in all of creation did God say that, as well being of use, they were 'pleasing to the eye' (Genesis 2.9). We would gratefully agree.

Nuthatch

Postscript

What Happened to Our Wood was written and at the copy-editing stage when my wife, Margaret, unexpectedly passed away. It was a huge shock, and even now the pain and void remains, but Margaret enjoyed the wood in her quiet unassuming way and would want me to publish this book. I know this because one of the very last things she did was to read the final draft, or have me read it to her when she was unwell and when we thought she only had flu. She particularly liked the last chapter. So the book has been dedicated to her memory.

In what proved to be the month before she died, I had told Margaret about two incidents that had newly arisen, and I add these to the postscript too. She smiled at both. They continue the almost uncanny associations arising from simply owning a 30-acre wood.

In November 2001 Upper Ashe Farm was sold as part of a larger estate to Formula 1 racing car champion, Jody Scheckter. This South African, and the last winner for Ferrari of the world title (in 1979) until the incomparable Michael Schumacher, is now our neighbour owning the field that abuts the boundary of Tanglewood and Nain's Copse. It is uncanny because of all the people who might have bought the field it is a famous Grand Prix driver and my son Stephen's passion—the son who drew some of the illustrations in chapters 8 and 9—is this sport, and Ferrari is his team. That's why I could write the details about Scheckter without even looking them up. And that's why Margaret and I, while once on holiday in northern Italy, took Stephen to Ferrari's home course of Monza and waited while he walked the entire 5.793 km circuit. We smiled that of all people who should become our new neighbour it is one of Ferrari's all time greats. And all we do is own a small wood in rural Hampshire.

In early December 2001 I kept a regular pre-Christmas speaking engagement at Winchester men's prayer breakfast. I was telling them about the wood and the discoveries (mostly based on what is recorded in chapter 3) as a kind of metaphor for the Christmas story. One of the items concerned the tiny mission hall on top of Litchfield tunnel which appeared and then disappeared from the cartographic record around 100 years ago. After the talk and after a nourishing if lipid-rich breakfast as a reward, one of the participants came up and suggested that this same mission hall had been moved to Eastleigh for mission work amongst railwaymen and then finally brought to Winchester for use by Highcliffe Evangelical Church. This coincidence was unbelievable: for years I have preached once of twice per year at this very church and to think that all the time I was inside the very building that once resided so close to our wood. However, delving in to the history of Highcliffe church failed to confirm this link. Their corrugated iron clad hall had been built as a pavilion in which to serve lunch for the visit of the Prince and Princess of Wales (later King Edward VII and Queen Alexandra) in 1883 to the southern agricultural show at Bar End. The hall was then moved to its present site for a mission to workmen cutting the railway tunnel, not at Eastleigh, but through the side of St Giles Hill on the edge of Winchester.

So no link after all, and for once an almost uncanny association is not established. It is time to end this book. And the final word: the great oak pollard at the corner of the old Ashe pightle, the finest tree in all the wood, now has a name:

Mum's Oak

Margaret Anne Evans
1947–2002